Across the Divide

Stories & Poems

by nicholas ferenczy

Weaver Designs

'Across the Divide – Stories & Poems'
December 2020
ISBN 9780995530522

Set in Century Gothic
& Garamond
Printed and bound in Great Britain
by Bell & Bain of Glasgow

British Library Cataloguing-in-Publication Data
A catalogue record for this book is available from
the British Library

Weaver Designs

For full contact details of the publisher
go to the website: www.weaverdesigns.co.uk

Contents

Intro

I thought it might help in the making sense of it and possibly be of interest to you to know how and why this book came about…

In part it's a response to the second book of stories and poems *The Bottle Kiln*, co-authored with Eva Bennett – largely 'set' in the North-West of England. The idea with *Across the Divide* was to leave the North and 'travel' to the Capital (and then perhaps return). The launch pad was to be an extended poem from towards the end of *The Bottle Kiln – Under Harecastle Hill* – which was to appear here near the start. Eventually it was decided all the material should be new. At this point, I haven't yet finished, so the process is still under way, and hard to pin down. But perhaps there is this concept working behind the scenes – subconsciously, if you like.

Certainly some of the pieces were written as specific contributions. But as anyone who writes will probably tell you, it is very much easier to write spontaneously for oneself rather than to a brief (even if the brief is self-imposed). So while having this overall concept in mind, poems (mostly) surfaced that were not necessarily done consciously 'for the cause'. I still wished for much of this to contribute to a connected whole somehow. It is the 'somehow' that becomes the creative pain – if an enjoyable one. One option is in the ordering of the material...

Obviously it doesn't have to come chronologically – as you'll see from the dates at the end of each. The order is up for grabs. But let's say the book is to have a structure – a beginning, middle and end. North-South-North? Hmm, perhaps. Perhaps not! In any case, how to 'travel'? How to get about? Narratives usually have characters we follow. But that is not how these were written, although, perhaps there are types that could appear in more than one, these are all distinct and yet might be connected… somehow!

Perhaps the so-far-ignored elephant in the room is the images. These are an important part of the communication. The words must stand first by themselves, but the pictures can work alongside. I think of them as like the scenery clocked through a train window on a journey. A person might look up from their smart phone, tablet or newspaper as they gaze out and let their thoughts meander. (Personally I never tire of just looking.) We all travel the same journey but the stuff out the window can lead your eye far away into the distance and then back down beside the railway track – it can even lead back into the carriage itself, which is somehow to break the narrative – probably the same way as does illustrating literally what is said by the text. Certainly images open up possibilities...

I learned from *The Bottle Kiln* that drawings and photo-based images work on us differently. Many of the drawings used in *The Bottle Kiln* have a friendly feel. But they can run the risk of making the thing look twee. There seemed to be a way that photos can be used that is far harder – darker, more alienating, disorientating – particularly when they push towards abstraction so that one is barely sure, or perhaps not at all sure, what is being looked at. Then can the text be put on the image or run alongside a visual strip. (And that is not without challenges regarding legibility or the spoiling of the visual impact of images or simply being super-obscure to the point of irrelevance.) But this filmic quality appeals to me greatly. For sure, the job of adding images makes the production feel like trudging up sand dunes, but with the writing complete and a few items illustrated one starts to get a sense of how it might go. So it is a bit like 'bootstrapping', and yet from a creative point of view, all up for grabs. That mightn't be so with traditional publishing – in part, my background also.

Traditionally, the production of an apparently similar book would involve a writer, an editor, artists and designers – all over-seen by a publisher. The publisher might have a house style and the book be produced in the house style. It might even be part of a series. Ultimately the publisher's drive is commercial – it has to sell to pay staff and meet overheads, etc, and make a bit of profit. But the hope would be that creative standards are as high as can be. No doubt there will be tensions within any publishing house as commercial and creative impulses clash. People see things differently – and that's not all bad. Decisions will be made at meetings and settled, production schedules drafted, deadlines set, launches arranged and so on. It might be down to certain powerful individuals to question some of the decisions and perhaps persuade colleagues to look again. (Meetings over covers would be a case in point.) But on the whole a publisher moves a bit like an oil tanker and is slow to turn. So is the traditional publisher mighty powerful but also vulnerable – as was Talos to Jason!

No doubt an editor would have a large input on the structure and the order of a similar-looking book to this. A designer would oversee the use of images and layout. The writer (out of house) would provide the raw-text-materials. (If I were lucky, that might be me held at a good arm's-length!) An artist/photograper would provide the raw-image-materials. But (thanks to digital technology) as our little renegade outfit (*Weaver Designs*) handles 'text, art, layout and publication' there remains the possibility of making changes at any stage – even writing/illustrating new material.

Creatively, that's powerful too, but dangerous – creatively powerful in that I can follow an idea uncompromisingly – there are no committees here. On the other side, there is the saying: 'many heads are better than one'! Mine might be poorly conceived. Plus, without production schedules, there is also the danger that it might become never-ending.

Traditionally, publishers were (and still are) gate keepers – seen as arbiters of taste, not letting through anything perceived as sub-standard. But that's a top-down authoritarianism that I believe is out-moded. (The same will be true I believe in government, education and trade.) I subscribe to grassroots creativity, censured only by a process of natural selection – readers' choices. *Weaver Designs* hasn't mega-publisher shed-loads of money to chuck at it. Instead we can give it time. But with little budget for sales and marketing, a project such as this has to go by word-of-mouth and open mic – slow and true! So the listeners and readers are most empowering of all.

The reason I mention all of this is because I wish people to realize this is a product of purely Indie publishing – a new animal, as in new-wave and punk, and it's not alone. As such, the creative process is full of exciting new possibilities. But back again to the problem of creating a whole...

As more possibilities emerge and multiply, one is faced again with an amorphousness – all possibility, no resolution – it can be ANYTHING so will be NOTHING! Then there are the cats...

Writing about cats is easy. While you are banging your head against the wall trying your hardest to squeeze out something that will solve your simultaneous equation – 5 poems about cats fall out! We like cats. They cheer us up. Stick 'em in. But where? – altogether as a chorus of cats, or sprinkled through as meandering miaoulers?

'Nature' is a theme that crops up in my work – deliberately from an uninformed and unreliable point of view. Where does that come? Is that perhaps 'the bit in the middle'? After all, the Capital and her provinces all touch on nature – it is common ground. One starts to think again about the concept of *Across the Divide* : a city itself can be divided – some of the worst poverty alongside crass wealth, for instance. The divisions are not merely regional. Divisions might be temporal or spatial, might pertain to love, to the psyche – even a self might be divided – perhaps we all are!

Should it remain amorphous so the connections are by way of resonances within text and image, discovered by the reader alone? (At this point, I realise that by writing this to you, I have just made the job of finishing it 100 times harder!) Any road, whether you start in the middle and go back, or go forwards from the start, you'll see what came out.

Now the book is reaching completion, and I have to say that since starting to write this intro, two events of enormous significance have occurred – one is the Corona virus (Covid 19) pandemic. The other event was the murder of black American, George Floyd, by a policeman on the streets of Minneapolis, US, and the global 'Black Lives Matter' protests and demonstrations that have followed. These, after 9/11 (chronologically, I mean) will no doubt prove to be defining events of the early part of this century.

In a way, never was the world more divided than it is at this moment, and yet in another, united too – in the common causes of fighting a pandemic and fighting racism. The enormity of these makes this little project seem like pure vanity and vanishingly small. But whatever's happening, that would always be the case. I hope you find something here...

Notes on form and reading...

As with *The Bottle Kiln*, I used the arbitrary rule of starting each line with a capital letter – so one would need to read across lines for sense. You might say that much of what is laid out as poetry simply isn't poetry. I wouldn't argue with that. I just write – it's not for me to say what it is. But I do know that writing in the form of short lines rather than as continuous prose somehow affects the delivery of the whole in terms of pace and rhythm – it becomes more musical. This makes many of these suitable to perform. And really, they should all be 'read out loud' even if only to oneself and silently in the mouth.

Again the text is big and spaced out so there is room for the images to run alongside as the pages are turned with momentum – so it might feel rather like the experience of glancing out through the train window while moving forwards. The little stories/vignettes – set in a different font with justified text – are written in a different way, and would be read more conventionally. (*Verdict* is a strange hybrid of the two. *Epilogue: The Secret River* is straight prose – like a magazine article.) In just a few, *Storm* and *Right over the Top*, for instance, the image(s) takes precedence, the words nudging (or tub-thumping, in the case of the latter!) the reader towards the image.

Nicholas Ferenczy June 2020

The content (text and images) of all the poems and stories is fictitious. Though some of the place names, postcodes and stations mentioned coincide with reality, the context in which they appear is purely fictitious and so these labels might be substituted for any arbitrarily chosen name. They should be taken to signify nothing in particular but to function as generic types. Similarly, buildings such as shops and cafes and those of institutions that appear in the text or images appear also in fictitious contexts – rather as found objects might in an assemblage or sampled sounds in a piece of electronic music. Unless otherwise stated, all the persons here are fictitious characters and any resemblance to persons living or deceased is purely coincidental.

Speaker's Cornered

It's, er, not open mic
It's a little shut down,
On you,
With no feedback.

Intro! Intro!
Excuse or apology?
(Say the title.
Say it again.)

Barely tall enough
Standing on ceremony.
I'd just like to say
I'd just like to say...
(Can you hear me at the back?)

Snogged on the gob
Speechless I was.
Yakety-yak.
A penny for your thoughts
Blah-de-blah. Etcetera.

One,
Big,
Yawn.
Like a lion
Gasping for meaning.

Lacking continuity
No, keepy-uppy,
Disrespecting history.
What a shame.
What a pity.

Too many words.
Take-away text.
Oh I forgot to tell you…
That needs a comma.

Sucker-punched in the gut
Winded by nonsense.
It made sense, when I wrote it.

Chased from the newsagents, I was,
By a hack writer with a pen,
Utilitarian prose trickling down his leg.
He says: ‘Hang on mate,
I haven’t finished your captions, yet!’
(Terribly pedestrian.)

Out of breath
Like a ran-out biro
With nothing to say.
Schticking like jam.
The bit in between.

Couldn’t make head nor tail
Folded it up,
Stuck it in an ashtray.
Now where do I start?
I was speechless!
I’ve got nothing to say…

May 2017

Thin String

There runs a thin string inside,
Up and down from heart to mind
Or, sometimes, front to back.
(From now to when?)
Now, like some innertube
Or Möbius strip
Living rubber, throbbing,
That might go on and on.
And then fine, like a filament
Of catgut sympathetically-tuned,
Stretched beyond what anyone
Ought to endure –
Nearly not a soul at all –
But one that,
If only we could open ourselves
So that the air would play across it,
Would sing a keening love song
Or killer's lament
So we would know the other,
As do we ourselves.

December 2018

A River

It started high up
And long ago,
No bubbling spring
Just a dampness
On a misty morning,
Dew squeezed out in hope
That it might not be dried
By midday sun,
But form a tear beside a cowslip
To run, between blades of grass,
In a Gloucestershire meadow
And somewhere meet a second
Then vanish,
Gone to ground
Until that ledge of clay
Beside a badger's sett,
From where it seeped again
Into a steady drip –
Cool and clear,
For a thousand years.

And yet, as if written into its being,
Was there always some division,
So the dribble split and split again,
Until, as in a web of finest woven lace,
Fine rivulets ran and crossed,
Okavango, Mekong, Yangtze –
Mighty deltas here in perfect miniature,
Long before the bluebells came.
The story's end it might have been
Except that, written in too,
As in a charter signed at Runnymede,
Was there to be a meeting
So the waters reconvened
At a secret place,
In solemn union,
Agreement as it were,
That it would be, a river.

Hah! There's ambition.
Drained by thirsty herd,
Passed over by frog and dragonfly –
Fosse – ditch – no more.
I might have said: 'I told you so!'
Where the ground lay hard
And parched, always thirsting
For a shower,
And you were nowhere to be seen –
You over-reach yourself.
River? Think first, how to be a stream.

But below the hill,
Two fields down –
In a dell, green with moss and fern
(Where wild orchids grow)
I heard your answer in a plash
Of waters, on a flattened stone,
Smoothed by these disgorgings,
As from mouth of garden god
But here no ornament:
Set pouring with divine purpose,
Gifted, by the ancient Earth itself.

Am I sorry to have doubted?
No! Gladdened –
Gladdened by your overflowing pool
That gives up your further course downstream
With gurgle of delight,
Like a joyful water-child at play,
Cradled in reeds,
Attended by willows,
Nurtured by the land.
I know your name,
History in liquid
And yet, here in your infancy,
Are you innocent and vulnerable.

I know you name,
But wonder how you'll grow
To slake a city's thirst,
Ablute its sins,
Float merchant fleets of fortune,
Fleets of war,
And change the destinies of men.

How will you grow –
Flash across the acres
As far as eye can see,
Make islands of churches,
Farms and settlements,
Churn, boil,
Tear bridge from footings,
Rage upon their ingenuity,
Surge upon barrier and embankment,
Hammer then, at the foundations
Of democracy?

Your mystery is a looping course
Ever-East, but by North and South –
And even West you go –
At every twist and turn
Seeking confluence,
And then – not to be subsumed,
But as one of noble line –
Receive a tribute,
And at the next,
And at the next,
As Derry, Ampney, Key
And Ray renamed –
Become your own.

I picked a buttonhole
Of Deadman's Bell
And on Lamas Day
At North Meadow,
Let my herds run free,
To graze beside you,
Among those plants and butterflies –
Marmalade and black – fritillary.

I drank Valerian from your banks
And slipped into a dream of long ago.
So through your surface did I pass,
Then deeper into ooze of mud
While around the lampreys swarmed,
With elvers, silver dace and sullen chub.

By caddis, leech and nymph
I touched a crusted blade
And twisted crown upon your bed
While by your banks at Battlefield,
There walked the ghosts of kings
Long since dead.

Then I awoke
And by weir and wheel
Tapped your power
And trapped your fish
And milled my corn –
At every wharf was industry,
Barges straining at the rope.
But by Kelmscott,
Printed on in willow green,
Woven into tapestry
Carved in stone and oak,
The few upheld
A mediaeval dream.

Fed by tributary veins
You course arterial
Through the body of land –
By dreaming spires
Where lovers lay upon the lawn
And heretics were put to torch
Taking life blood to the capital
Wherein dwells the mind of man,
Great pool of pride and folly.

Far beneath the London clay
As I await the blast
Of subterranean winds
And points of light and dreadful rumble
That will take me to my journey's end,
I see your glistenings
On the walls above
And hear the tick, drip, tick, drip
Of you Old Man,
Seeping through the layers of time.

March 2018

see also 'Epilogue: The Secret River' page 185

Room 101

'Don't do that!' said she
As I threw in,
With one still in,
(And not into the bin
But into the black rubbish sack),
A half-empty sandwich pack.
'You might attract a rat.'

'Only yesterday,' (said I),
'Did I see one as big as a cat.'
She said: 'Where was that?'
I said: 'On a programme about Gujarat.'
Said she: 'You stupid prat!
I thought you meant here in the flat.'

'Did you know,' said I,
Reciting a stat,
'That in London,
For everyone there sat,
Within two feet of them, is a rat?'

She said: 'Why do you keep
Mentioning a rat?'
I said: 'All right,
I'll keep it under my hat.'

(There came a rustle from the sack.)
'What was that!?' said she.
'Just a settling,' said I (with tact),
Putting on a cool act,
While a shiver ran up my back.

'A settling?' said she,
What is that, to be exact?'
'Well,' said I, 'it's like when something flat,
Such as a plastic sandwich pack,
Has been folded
And starts springing back.'

'Not one little bit
Do I like the sound of that,' (said she).
'Springing?
Go and fetch the bat!'
'The bat!? What for?' said I.
'Because you can creep over
And give it a whack!'

'That's inhumane
They won't attack
(Well, not unless cornered)
Poor *Rattus Norvegicus*!
Scared of them we might be,
–They're far more afraid of us!'

'Anyway, there is no…'
(I was about to say 'rat'
When there came a visible
Lurching from the sack.)
'Right that's it!'
Said she said, running out
And peering back in through a crack.

Cut a long story short
I got the bat
And went over
And gave it a whack
– several in fact –
And opened it wide
So she could see inside
And said: 'There look, see,
Entirely rat-free!
It's the pack's to blame,
Come on let's get back to the game.'
(There being nothing on TV
We were playing Scrabble, you see.)

'Can you go?' said I.
'Maybe,' said she.
'But it's a pity,
With one more I'd have four.
But I'll settle for that
Not a 'tra!' or some 'art'
Just an 'R-A-T' spells rat!'

May 2017

Karamac's On the Road

I met you in a mars bar
Across the milky way.
We flew on flying saucers
To make our getaway.

You were my dolly mixture,
Milk teeth and cherry lips.
You were my midget gem
With jelly-baby hips.

Your hair was candy floss,
Mine was curly wurly.
We rode white mice to humbug town,
Tho evening, it was early.

We dined on pink foam shrimps,
Fruit Salad, acid drops,
We paid with funny money
And Black Jack called the cops.

They sat us down on kula cubes
Those American hard gums,
Pulled on candy cigarettes,
Said they'd caught a pair of bums.

We flumped down in separate jars
As they screwed on the lids,
Said we'd languish liquorice long
For all sorts we never did.

But they'd put us in with fizz wiz,
And a sherbert fountain,
With bubblegum and wham –
Enough to shift a mountain.

In a cloud of rainbow dust
The confectioner's was gone.
We did the aniseed twist
As we danced into the sun.

November 2018

Mind the Gap

Indoor railway –
City hollowed out ingeniously
From beneath –
Mice in their million hordes
From West Ruislip to Theydon Bois.
Under the river
Down in the bowels
Rumble and warm wind
Sets a plastic bag rolling –
Desert tumble weed –
Beneath the rails.

West End-bound.
Reading readers heads down,
Thinking thinkers eyes shut –
Avoid eye-contact at all cost.
What does she do?
What did he do?
Where are they going?
Revellers unable to focus
On station names
Through smeared glass,
Will slumber, rouse and
Miss their stops.
But not yet...

You lean against the motion,
Don't even need to hang on –
Experienced sea legs
Accommodating every twist and turn
Around the Plague pits,
That send tourists sprawling.
You know where every door
Coincides with archway
To stairs for exit or line change.
It's your city...

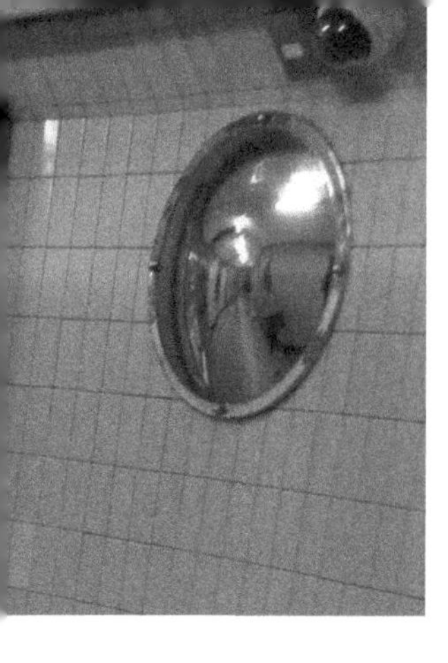

Out you go,
Down steps inset with bronze treads
Against the wear and tear
Of millions, through tiled tunnels,
By mysterious subterranean doors,
Later, by a snogging couple,
That might have been sheltering
From The Blitz, at Aldwych.
But not yet,
Not... yet...

On to the platform.
Spot for a dead-cert seat
Ignored in favour of mid-platform,
Where crowding tourists
Turn their A-Zs this way and that,
Check and check the indicator,
Whose destination
Flips back and forth,
Arrival time counting down –
All green but ripe for the picking.

To the agreed spot
Northern over Piccadilly –
Promising so much
When you've a little cash!
A couple of pints in
The Crown and Two Chairmen
And then round the corner
To where that old lush,
'Gerry the Bradford Millionaire',
In his camel hair coat,
Props up the bar,
Asking to borrow a tenner
From the uninitiated.
Past the whispering doorway
Of some dive,
By red-light-beckoning alleys
With their flashing signs a blur
And maybe 'him' or 'her'?
To Old Compton Street
And the Fab-Four tribute band
That has everyone
Howling at the tops of their voices –
Just a little cash is all it takes.
Stay focused!

You're a needle in a haystack –
CCTV has no chance –
Next door down, as agreed
Your team mates:
Jen – all care and consideration,
For 'poor Joe'. 'Poor Joe' –
Playing his part to perfection –
(Should have gone to RADA,
Our Joe!)

***"Please stand clear
of the closing doors"***

Here they come –
Joe stumbling, bumbling
Up the aisle;
Jen all-supportive, caring,
All eyes on them.
'Sorry! He can't help it.'
(Offers for seats declined).
Then by you,
Where he turns it on,
So you can almost feel them say:
'Don't talk to me!
Please, please, don't talk to ME!'
And Joe stops,
And starts talking to some guy,
Who smiles and apologizes:
'Sorry' – he can't hear
Because of the 'noisy train'.
'C'mon Joe,' says Jen, coaxingly,
Gently trying to ease Joe away.
But Joe won't leave it –
Instead, turns it up – mouth twisting,
'Idiotic' words drawling out,
Slow and incomprehensible –
A magnet for every nearby
Ear and eye,
So it is as if there is
Nothing in the world
But this poor strange 'boy',

So time stands still for you,
Freeze-framed by pure genius.
And all you have to do
Is dip your hand gently inside her coat,
Take the purse cleanly,
Pass it unseen to the waiting hand behind
and, as the train slows and stops,
Get out and walk calmly away.

"Doors opening."

May 2020

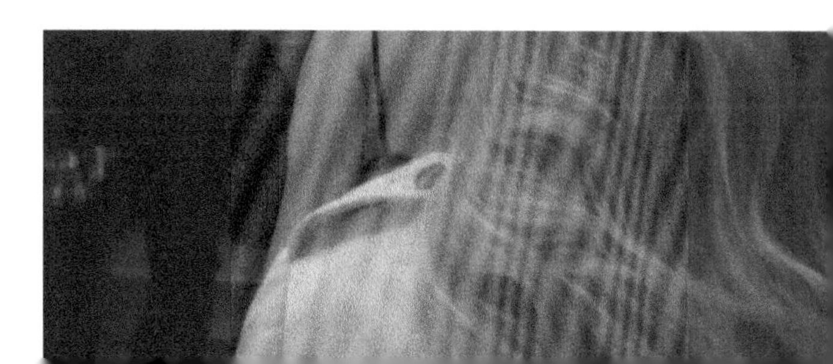

Cat up a Tree

The world must stop turning
Let everything be
Drop what you're doing
There's a cat up a tree

Turn off the grill
Come here right now
Who can ignore
Such a pitiful meow?

Fetch a fireman, a ladder,
A basket, a rope,
She's ever-so high,
We must stand here and hope…

She doesn't go higher
She's young and not skilled,
If she falls from the top
She's sure to be killed.

Encouraging words,
Advice how to climb,
Prayers she won't use
All of her nine.

Her first is aborted
A well-meant attempt –
A courageous if foolish
Head-first descent.

Next comes a shimmy –
Working tail-first
Not one of her best
Nor one of her worst.

Back up again
Now stuck at the top
Tired and frightened
She looks like she'll drop

Then slowly but slowly
By twig, branch and bough
Does she start to come lower
And let out a meow!

Call for the basket
To be placed just-so,
Where it must always be
To finish her show.

April 2020

Lord Lucan, in the Pantry, with the Lead Pipe (allegedly)

Possibly to the tune of 'The Laughing Policeman'

Strolling by our chippy
When I spied a charming gent,
Moustache was waxed and bristling,
Knees were nicely bent.
Three-piece suit was Savile Row
Backgammon was his game,
I'd swear I'd seen him in the news –
What was that fellow's name?

Oh Lord Lucan,
It's really time to dash,
No time to mess with brilliantine
And grooming your moustache.
Oh Lord Lucan
There's no turning back,
They've found the bandaged lead pipe
And the nanny in the sack.

Sitting in the barber's chair
Waiting for a trim
Turning to my neighbour
To have a word with him, I was
When all at once
I thought: 'Hello – I'm sure I know that face!'
He turned and said 'Cheerio!'
And bounded from the place.

Oh Lord Lucan,
It's really time to dash,
They're accusing you of murder
And of nicking petty cash.
Oh, Lord Lucan
There's no turning back,
They've found the bandaged lead pipe
And the nanny in the sack.

A flutter on the gee-gees,
A scratchcard for 'the wife',
And once a week plays Spot-the-Ball –
He lives a sheltered life. (He does.)
The certificate is signed,
We all presume him dead.
The detectives all retired,
Play Cluedo now instead.

Oh Lord Lucan,
It's really time to dash,
Leaving victim, means and motive,
Really was so rash.
Oh Lord Lucan
There's no turning back...

"Okay Chief, we're gathered 'poolside',
Now open up the envelope
And let's see what you've got..."

"Ah, it's just as I'd suspected all along, Sergeant...
Lord Lucan, in the Pantry, with the lead pipe!"

"Ah, but hang on a mo, Chief. Where is he?"

"Er, ah, good point Sergeant. Maybe he's down here.
I'll just take a look...
Nope, he's not under the carpet."

"Maybe he's hiding behind
Your toast and marmalade, Sir...
Shall I have a quick shufti?"

"Be my guest, Sergeant –
You know, I'm really quite enjoying my retirement."

...They've found the bandaged lead pipe
And the nanny in the sack!

Evening all.

March 2017

MARM

A Sad Case of the Alsatian Blues

Sad case hand-me-down,
Given to him by his stepfather
After early-retirement
From the Civil Service,
Shiny red-brown leather,
Brass clasp snapped shut –
Dutiful but useless
In a job that did not require
The carrying of papers.
Held then, only as
A token of self-esteem,
To remind him, he has a job.
A sad case with a dreadful
Hole at the corner,
From where the stitching has gone,
That might let slip
Something important,
As might his stepfather's mind,
When he'd taken early retirement.

Now, here, on The Tube after work,
The stepson sits
On a Friday night
After a pint or two,
A little worse for wear.
The sad case under his legs,
Pressed to the seat.
Years and years later,
He would think:
'I should have listened,
When he'd said:
"And just for a moment
I didn't know where I was"
And believed, and understood,
And shown some sympathy!'
But not yet. Not now.
Now wrapped up only
In selfish projects.

He opens the case
And looks inside
To check it hasn't slipped out
Through the hole –
Loose leafs written in blue biro,
Mostly here on the Northern Line,
Each new phrase surfacing
As a warm glow of inspiration,
Sentences polished
In and out of the city,
Each one taking him
Further from his destination –
The novel that goes backwards.
(If he did but know it,
But he didn't, not then.)

He shuffles the papers
Up to the safe end,
Away from the hole
And shuts the clasp with a click
And brightening, thinks:
'Homeward bound.
Friday night and not even 8 o'clock.
You sad case!'

The restaurant is Chinese –
A smart one, just round the corner
From his digs, recommended
In the London rag as being 5-star –
Mercifully quiet for a Friday,
Just a couple of other diners.
He pushes the shabby case
Well under the table
With the toe of his shoe,
And makes a show of ordering –
A bit of bluster to conceal the fact
He's ashamed to eat alone.

The food, too good for one,
Goes under-appreciated,
While he toys with a lager
And stumbles through
The easy crossword,
Resorting to searching up the alphabet,
Unable to finish.
He tries to attract the owner's attention
For the bill and does, but not straight way.
(They do that, don't they, when it's you?)
Bill in hand,
He takes the case, the sad case,
From under the table
And goes to the counter –
To where the owner's polishing glasses,
Spacing and aligning each one
On a shelf above the till.

All at once, he feels self-conscious,
Incongruous – like a dreadful fraud,
Absurd briefcase under his arm –
And takes the pen
And signs carelessly with a flourish,
So that when the owner checks it
Against the card, he shakes his head,
And says the match is not good.
'Could he sign again, please?'

Wave of indignation passes
Through the young man's muzzy head.
He thinks: 'Why should I?
I've already done it.'
Says: "It'd be just a bad as the last,
There's no point."
The owner says that, if he will not sign,
He'll have to call the police.
The stepson thinks:
'It is my card. It is my life.
I am who I say I am.'
And says: "Go on then."
And sits back down.

Now the owner's talking on the phone
Reading from the card
And occasionally looking up at him.
The couple in the window,
Engrossed in each other,
Haven't noticed.
He waits. And thinks. And waits.
A party of diners arrive,
The owner bustles about them.

"When will the police be here?"
"Soon!"
But the police do not arrive –
Bigger fish to fry on a Friday night, perhaps?
The card – his card – is on the counter.
He has signed for the food he's eaten.
He gets up, walks to the counter,
Picks up the card and makes for the door,
But somehow, impeded by the briefcase,
Becomes trapped between two doors
As if in a comedy,
While the owner bounds across and,
With a deft flick of the wrist, breaks the card
And pulls it from his hand.
He takes a key on a chain from his belt
Locks the front door
And then runs – runs – up the stairs.
The stepson goes slowly back to his table,
Puts the briefcase on the floor
And sits back down, resignedly.

An Alsatian dog – large and shaggy
Like the ones that jump
Through flaming hoops,
Scale wooden walls and then
Pull a running man down by his wrist –
Appears at the foot of the stairs
Followed by the owner
Who instructs it to: "Stay!"
And now the diners ARE looking –
Glancing across at him,
Then to the dog, and whispering.
The young man tells the owner:
"It's an outrage!"
The owner tells him to:
"Wait for the police."

A smart, middle-aged man asks:
"Is everything okay?"
And offers to pay for the food.
The young man says: "No thanks. It's okay.
There's just been a misunderstanding."
But he would appreciate a cigarette.
The man returns and
Places a box of matches
And three cigarettes on the table.
Outside, prospective diners
See a guard dog looking at them
Through the glass of a locked door,
And have to be let in,
By an apologetic owner,
Who gestures towards
The 'awkward customer' –
Solitary man at a table with a briefcase,
Smoking cigarettes.

10:00pm on a Friday,
No longer homeward bound,
But caught up in some kind of siege,
The young man finally loses patience
And tells the owner
He's going to call the police himself!
Which he does,
From a payphone on the wall,
Dialling 999 as the only number
He can think of
And is put through,
Not to some local station,
As he'd hoped, but to Scotland Yard.
Inspired by the snowballing absurdity
He hears himself say:
"I'm being held hostage
In a Chinese restaurant
In Finchley and they've put
An Alsatian dog on the door."
At the other end of the line,
A world-weary voice tells him,
"We'll send someone over." –
As if this sort of thing
Is always happening,
Which it probably is.

Finally a car pulls up outside
Flashing blue, but no sirens.
Job done, dog scampers upstairs,
Owner lets them in enthusiastically –
Like he's bagged a bad 'un,
Just a formality now,
For them to collect –
Policeman and policewoman.
They question the young man
And, convinced he is who he says he is,
Return the credit card – bent.
Then catching sight of something
On the floor next to the table,
The policeman says:
"Is this your bag, sir?"

"Yes," he says.
The policeman looks from the briefcase
Back to the young man and says:
"D'you mind if we take a look inside?"
The stepson takes up the case and opens it,
Pulling apart the sides so that it gapes
Like the mouth of a great gutted fish
And holds it out for inspection, as if to say:
"There, there you are,
I'm baring my very soul to you,
Take a good look, if you will!"
The policeman peers in and,
Seeing no more than scraps of paper,
And his own boot through a dreadful hole
At the corner – a hole that might let slip
Something important,
If only there was anything
Important enough to let slip –
Concludes the bag is not a threat,
And says: "Thank you, sir."
The young man is surprised,
After all the trouble he's caused,
When the policewoman asks,
If he'd like to press charges for
Being held against his will.
He says he wouldn't,
But can't resist a:
"'Hope you're bloody-well satisfied!"
Directed at the owner,
That brings forth a cautioning:
"Now then, sir!" from the policeman.

11pm Friday night homeward bound,
Swinging the case,
The sad sad case
In a carefree manner, he thinks:
'Pity, food was great,
But can't go back there again.'

August 2017

Not Quite Outside

There are those stairs in the old foyer,
The familiar reception area,
And the climb
That will take him
To the place he once knew.
But it is always on the mezzanine,
From where he looks down
And sees where he's been
And looks up to where he has yet to go,
That stairs don't connect as stairs should –

A bannister bars the way
So he must step across –
Always he must use the staircase
In some strange way, that no-one else,
Who goes about their daily business –
Laughing and joking, seemingly carefree,
Chatting about the weekend,
Or last night's TV – ever does.

To him, the move appears at first
As if a little awkward only,
Not 'wrong' – but like the knight's move in chess.
(After all, why would a staircase
Be there at all, if it was not 'right'?)

This decisive point,
Which connects where he is,
With what is desired,
Is absolute in its logic –
Rigorous as a conditional: 'if-then'.

Sometimes the top step
Ends against a wall,
While the first of the next flight
Emerges from the wall across the way –
As though the landing
Had been removed.

Sometimes, the stairs bring him
To a little landing
From where he sees,
The underside of the next flight
Continuing overhead,
And he wonders: 'How did I go wrong?
How do other people use this?'

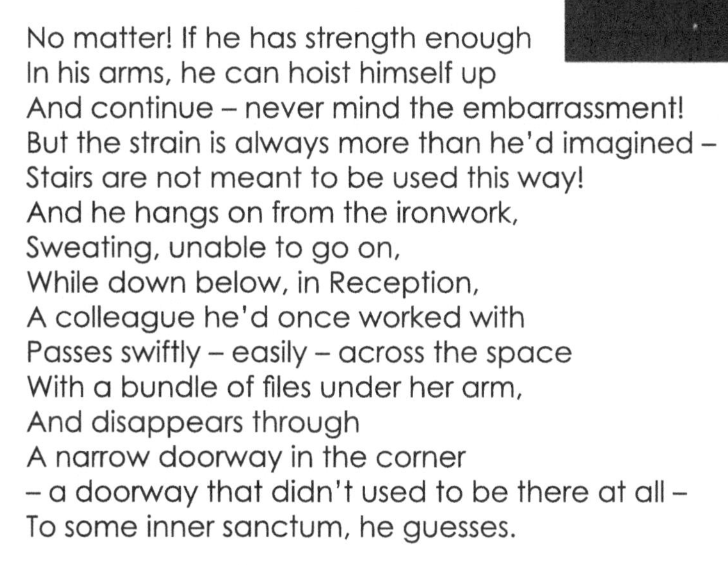

No matter! If he has strength enough
In his arms, he can hoist himself up
And continue – never mind the embarrassment!
But the strain is always more than he'd imagined –
Stairs are not meant to be used this way!
And he hangs on from the ironwork,
Sweating, unable to go on,
While down below, in Reception,
A colleague he'd once worked with
Passes swiftly – easily – across the space
With a bundle of files under her arm,
And disappears through
A narrow doorway in the corner
– a doorway that didn't used to be there at all –
To some inner sanctum, he guesses.

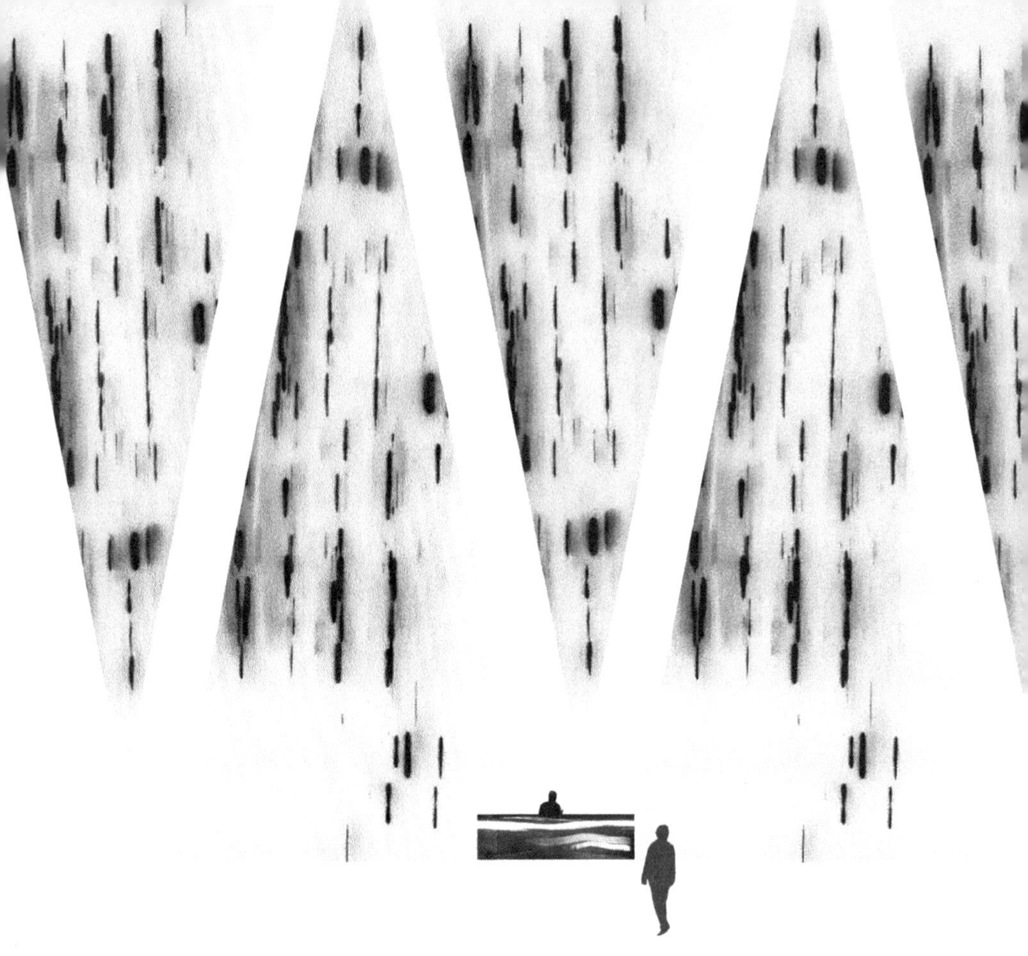

Releasing his grip and stepping down now,
He has a sudden realization.
A wave of relief washes over him –
'Ah, I see!' (he says) 'They've changed it all!'
He walks down and has a chat
With the receptionist on the desk,
Who confirms, with a brisk
But friendly and detailed description
Of the works (all plated-glass,
Tiles, hi-tech lighting) that this is:
'Such an improvement on what once was.'
'Look, d'you see,' (he says to himself)
'How easy it all becomes,
If you just stop trying.'

His ex-colleague appears
From the doorway,
And now he expects
This new bubble of optimism
To be pricked by some barbed remark:
'What are you doing here?
We thought you'd gone for good!'
Or some such, but not a bit!
Instead, asks him how long he's in town for,
Says they must have a drink and catch up,
Suggests they meet at her place at 8.
'See – see how easy it is,
When you just stop trying!'

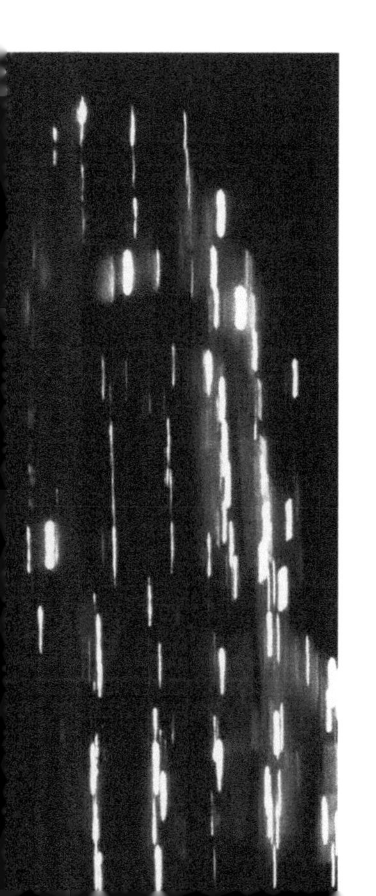

Later, that evening,
Outside her apartment block,
He thinks: 'She'll know what's going on.
We were on the same side, me and her –
She'll take me up that staircase –
Make all the necessary introductions –
All is not lost. It can be done.'

He presses the buzzer.
She tells him to come up.
But when he steps in through the door
He sees dark cells – arranged
As in the chambers of a revolver –
Lifts, one per flat, that will shoot him up,
But with barely room enough to fit,
So that he must adopt the fetal position,
Knees under chin, legs-cramping,
That brings on a cold sweat at his back –
A sweat so icy he knows, he must be mistaken
In thinking he is where he is –
Not in the foyer of an apartment block,
But somewhere very nearly outside –
Very nearly, but not quite, outside.

He surfaces voluntarily from sleep
Pulls the covers over,
And then goes back in, back down,
Down – like a miner seeking a seam of truth
Or a diver searching deep
For a pearl once glimpsed and,
Reaching nearly where he was,
Finds himself at a diner table
At the end of dinner,
As they're saying their goodbyes –
A satisfactory end to a good meeting,
And yet the essential point, missed.
But 'It's okay,' she says, she'll 'drop him an email.'
Now he must catch the Tube
And return home.
But there is the chill at his back...
Nearly outside but not quite.

Metropolitan lines crossing
At a junction under the city
Confirmed by the singing of wheels
Slicing the points
And the deep rumble
Of an approaching train.
He sees his feet on oily stones between tracks –
Between the tracks, not on the tracks –
But surely, not a good place to be?!
To the side, in the wall,
Is a window begrimed by under-city filth
From where there shows a dim light –
Some workman's hut.
He steps across the track
And passes in through a brick archway.

There is a small table and chair
And a kettle on a stove,
As if for one man, only.
But not for him.
He feels the floor tremble.
Carriage windows flash by
As the train passes immediately outside.
Here is temporary shelter only.
But if he can follow the rails safely
They'll lead him to the station platform nearby.
Because the logic between where he is
And what is desired, is absolute,
Rigorous, like a conditional: 'if-then'.

He wonders: were he to walk on the track,
Facing the trains,
Stepping aside only when one came,
Would he be safer
Than to walk between the tracks?

Two pinpoints of light
Approach slowly round the curve
And there comes the zing of wheels
Scything points.
He tries to follow the gleam of steel
Where he walks, to see if it meets
The oncoming train.
But somewhere between,
The light is lost to the dark.
There is no reference, no datum
Against which the danger
Might be measured.
He feels a chill at his back,
And remembers that danger comes
From both in front and behind,
And turns to see a train
Yet some way off
That will pass safely beside him –
A fact that confirms this is not
Some construct of his mind
Where his worst fears are realized,
But a parallel reality
Of indeterminate chance and truth,
Over which he can exercise freewill.

He returns to the front,
Where the lights are closer now, brighter
Much brighter. He has a choice –
One that if correctly made
Will ensure his survival
Because the logic which connects
Where he is with what he desired
Is absolute like a conditional: 'if-then'.
He remembers how easy it all becomes
If he just stops trying,
If he just stops trying.

Now, but slowly, he opens his eyes,
To where the light is closer still –
Coming through the curtains,
The light of a new day.

June 2017

SW7

Like some village halt,
Is South Ken. Station,
Where valanced canopies,
Summer sky-blue and white,
Cover us as we alight
For our perambulation.

We face a flower stall
Where five ways meet –
The Old Brompton
And Harrington Roads,
Cromwell Place,
Pelham and Thurloe Streets.

Let's go by 'The Hoop and Toy',
Where museum experts drink,
Small-talking rocket science,
Our evolving Earth,
And fossil bones
Of creatures long extinct.

And head East, by haunt
Of KGB spies, celebrities,
Proms conductors
From the Albert Hall,
Dining on escallopes,
Inside Café Daquise.

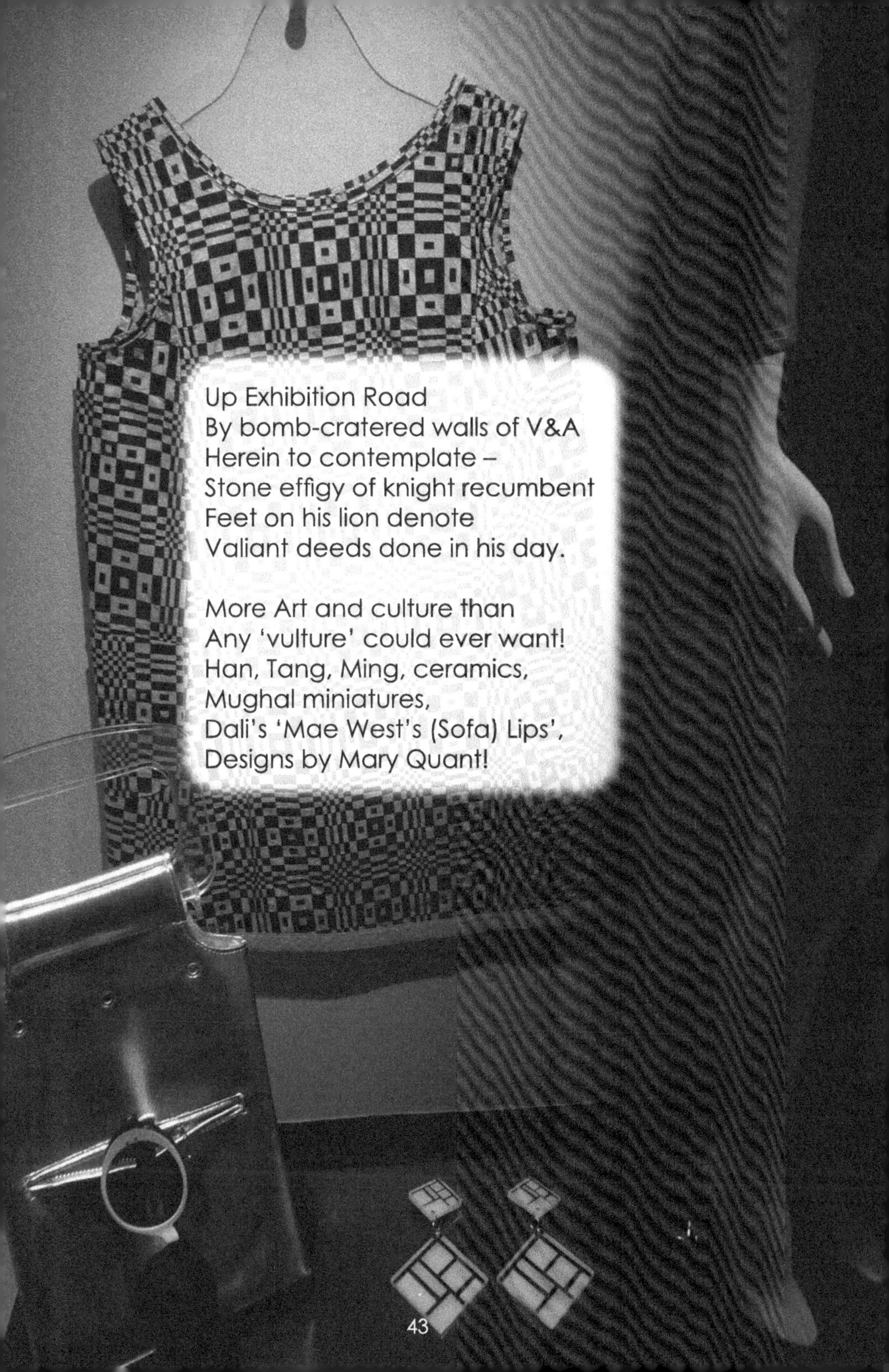

Up Exhibition Road
By bomb-cratered walls of V&A
Herein to contemplate –
Stone effigy of knight recumbent
Feet on his lion denote
Valiant deeds done in his day.

More Art and culture than
Any 'vulture' could ever want!
Han, Tang, Ming, ceramics,
Mughal miniatures,
Dali's 'Mae West's (Sofa) Lips',
Designs by Mary Quant!

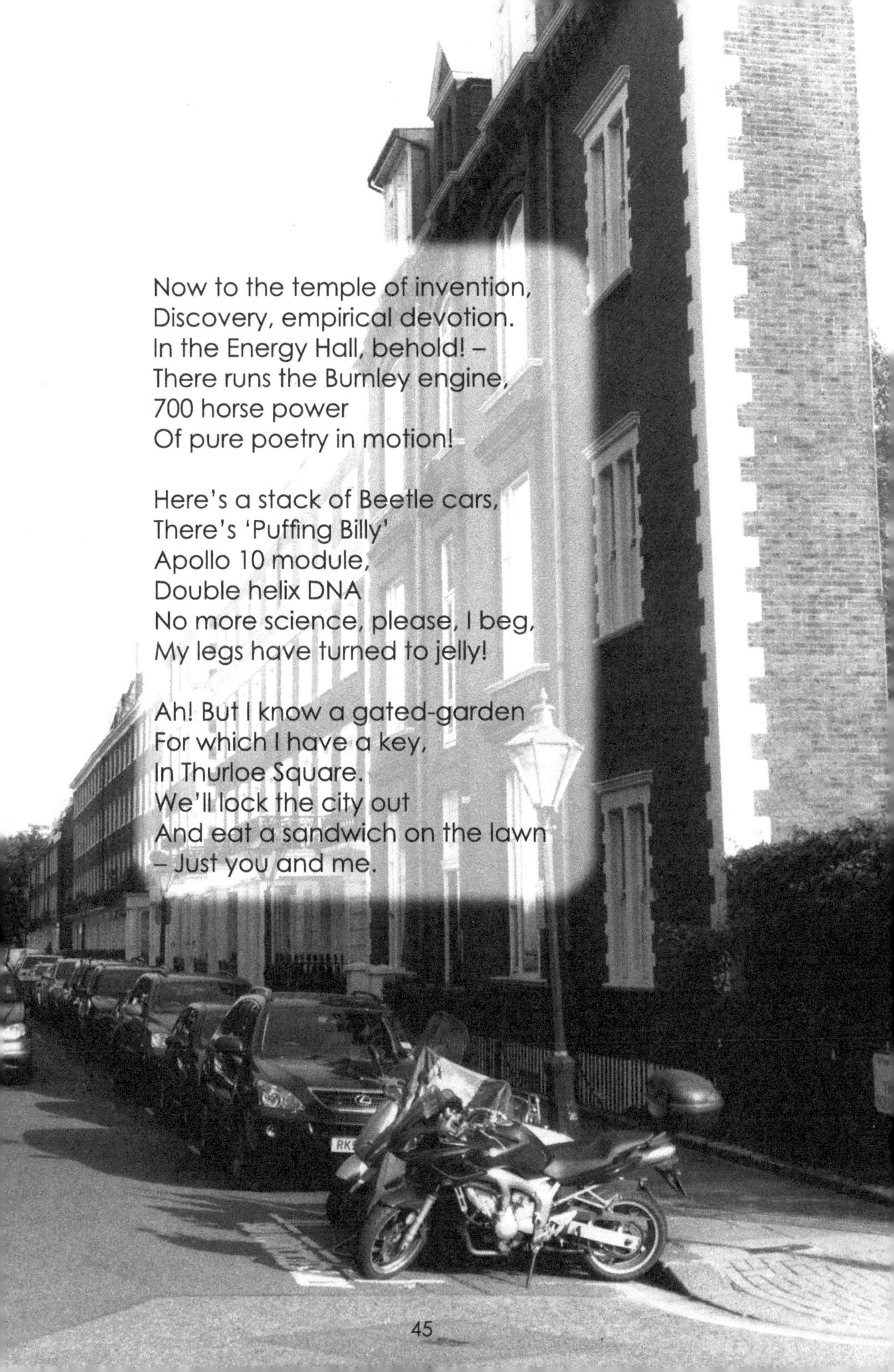

Now to the temple of invention,
Discovery, empirical devotion.
In the Energy Hall, behold! –
There runs the Burnley engine,
700 horse power
Of pure poetry in motion!

Here's a stack of Beetle cars,
There's 'Puffing Billy'
Apollo 10 module,
Double helix DNA
No more science, please, I beg,
My legs have turned to jelly!

Ah! But I know a gated-garden
For which I have a key,
In Thurloe Square.
We'll lock the city out
And eat a sandwich on the lawn
– Just you and me.

In Christies auction house
You say: "If I'm not mistaken,
Across the way is Reece Mews
Where there is the studio
Of the artist that painted this!
It belonged to Francis Bacon."

Screaming crimson mouths
More of hell than heaven,
Orange of Saharan sand,
Contorting figures,
Oil-black pools of shadow,
Made there at number seven.

Not far beyond is the 'En-Aitch-Em'!
But we've done with education –
For today at least the whale can wait
And opt for beer instead
On the way back to
South Ken. Station.

But so enriched are we –
Our minds fizzing with SW7 –
We talk and drink and laugh
Until the moon and stars
Are up and over us
And it is past eleven!

August 2019

The Piano Tuner

Somewhere off the Harrington Road is there a turning that, were you to take it, would bring you into a cobbled mews – one of the many thereabouts – strange little enclaves whose quiet calm and privacy are so immediate and at odds with the well-beaten highways left just yards behind, that they seem almost magical. Here are narrow-fronted, white-washed houses with jap black trimmings of drain pipes, lamp holders, queer metal fastenings, window railings, wall-hugging wisteria and – under shuttered ground-floor windows – borders of neat planters with bay trees and clipped box hedging – all bijou and chic enough. I guess it is the ad-hoc patchwork of design so unlike the familiar uniformity of our suburban streets, or even the elegant townhouses thereabouts, that appeals to our modern sensibilities as quaint! But of course, this appearance is just a result of original function – as stabling.

Here in the 18th Century would the owner, from the remote splendour of his house on the main street, operate a bell to ring in the servants' quarters – signal to ready horse and carriage for his jaunt up to the city. In short, these buildings were the garages of their time (even then the term 'mews' referring back centuries to out-buildings where royalty housed their falcons). If they no longer serve that purpose, they retain that air of 'careless-neglect-in-the-planning-of' – though now most, having been converted by one or other of the many swish London architects' consultancies, are meticulously maintained and go on the property market for somewhere around £2,000 a square foot.

You might wonder who'd live in such a house: an author, perhaps – but a successful one, whose international best-sellers could afford her such an abode; or a writer of musicals with a string of West-End hits behind him; a retired émigré, perhaps, formerly employed by one of the nearby embassies who has (so it is said) a shady past that no one seems able to recollect. There's probably a well known actor, an icon of the catwalk, an artist or two, but no doubt the owner of many a mews house these days lives outside the UK – Monaco, Moscow, New York, Dubai – their properties checked over by hired-hands, otherwise standing empty until such time as they or some family member flies in to Heathrow. For sure it was in this mews that there had once lived a piano tuner.

Just in case you are young enough to be thinking on career paths, I should be clear that it was not by his profession that Peter Fairbright came to own the house. His family home had been in West Sussex and his parents had bought the mews house (at a time when such properties could still be picked up for a song) as a base for his mother to use when she came up to work (then more frequently) at the BBC. Then in the 1960s the son had come to London as a young engineering student at one of the university colleges, intending to stay only for the time it took to complete his studies. But, as with so many movers to the Capital, things hadn't gone according to plan and 20 years on saw him still living there.

Neither had Fairbright planned to be a piano tuner. As a student he enjoyed music – listening to it but more so, playing in a rock band, finding that a more attractive prospect than his studies. At first a few lectures were missed as late nights spent doing support slots at the likes of The Marquee and The Roundhouse took their toll. When the register was taken in the first lectures of the morning, it was always Fairbright's name that went unanswered – the lecturer bobbing his head around the room to see if its owner wasn't tucked away and just hadn't heard. Occasionally, when he wasn't sleeping off the excesses of some gig, he'd show. But it was clear from his lack of engagement in set problems and practicals that his means to keep up was slipping away. Then there came the time when the calling out of his name followed by the question: "Has anyone seen Fairbright?" was met by smiles and knowing glances – with the approval of one who has just heard a joke, the joke being that the 'anyone' might now extend universally. 'Understanding, sympathetic' letters put out to his parents' address made no difference. Fairbright had dropped out.

Make no mistake, he wasn't stupid or lazy – he wouldn't have got into this prestigious university college had he been so. He was practical and resourceful and naturally curious about things. One afternoon while plunking out a melody on the upright that stood in the corner of the living room – an old Chappell that had been there since the very first day his mother had moved in – the idea came to him to try to tune it. A couple of hours later, armed with a book from Chelsea Library and one or two improvised tools, saw him listening intently as he worked his way up the strings. It was this tinkering that discovered a natural aptitude and good ear for the task, as by teatime he was able to repeat the right-hand phrase, so that it sounded exactly as it should. So did he fall into his trade by chance.

Living alone and being a man of modest means, it generated enough to keep the wolf from door. There were the many uprights that stood against the walls of halls and sitting rooms of private houses and flats between here and SW3. These would be tuned only occasionally – perhaps when the owners (who never touched them) were reminded by the attempts of some visiting neice or nephew stumbling through their latest grade 1 piece and creating such a clamour, that they really ought to 'get the damned thing tuned'!

Some trade came by way of the baby grands of swankier apartments towards Knightsbridge and Kensington High Street, where host or guest at some after-prom soirée would sit and dazzle friends and acquaintances with a mini-recital, or more likely just about hang on by their fingertips to their party piece, leaving their audience stunned (not always for the good). But the bread and butter stuff came from college music departments.

Here were the uprights of practice rooms – Yamahas and Danemanns – often instruments that had been sorely abused by students, thoughtlessly if not deliberately, setting down their plastic cups of hot drinks from the vending machine on their lids, leaving there in the polish indelible rings or, committing that most heinous of practice-room crimes – worse even than smoking in the first place – the resting of a cigarette on the keys of the upper octave while distractedly trying to play some passage that took just a little longer than it took their freshly-lit Marlborough to burn from tip to keys, only to be snatched up to leave a nicotine-coloured scar that would forever remain as evidence of their crime – until that is, Fairbright was called in to make good. (His skills extending to renovation and a little French polishing.)

Once in a blue moon would he have the privilege of preparing a concert grand for a performance – a Steinway, Bechstein or Bluthner – usually in an emergency, if the technician attached to the institution had been taken ill. Apparently, his name was still on the books at the Royal Albert Hall as a possible stand-in tuner because he had, 15 years before, prepared a concert grand for a performance of some musique concrète by one of the lesser-known East German composers of the avant garde.

And so things might have gone well enough for Fairbright. But as anyone will tell you, family fortunes can change and usually do. With one generation by youth, energy and luck might prospects be raised for the good of all, as resources accumulate and a family goes from strength to strength. But as Fairbright (as a student of engineering) knew well enough, the Second Law of Thermodynamics prevails, so that apart from these little pockets of high activity and strivings rewarded with decent living and happiness is there a steady attrition of the means to maintain control, as family members age and weaken, and the energy and funds to battle against the inevitable drain away – that is increasing entropy! So, first did Fairbright's father become ill and pass, and then his mother's health decline, before she too left this earth.

Fairbright had been very emotionally attached to his mother and loved her dearly. He took her passing particularly hard. He'd always hoped to find some way to restore the family's fortunes through his own efforts and hoped that this might be done in his parents' lifetime, so they could see it and by doing so, have their minds eased a little. This had not been possible. He began to see that through his own shortcomings and indiscipline as a student and his selfish indulgence playing music – at which he wasn't really even very good – he'd undone much of what they'd worked a lifetime to put in place.

He remembered a time his mother had tried to talk sense into him: 'Peter, you can't do everything. You must decide: is it music or engineering – you can't just be a dilettante – we don't have the money for it. Your father is furious – he thinks I'm mad just coming here to talk to you. You need to sort yourself out before it ends in a catastrophe!' Well it had, and now this burden of guilt weighed heavily on him.

It was during these moments of melancholy that his overly-active, enquiring mind was apt to spiral off tangentially into whirling fractals of thought that took him very quickly beyond the common orbit of most peoples. He knew he was over-thinking things again. That was the problem, he thought to himself, as he tinkered with a badly out-of-tune Petrof. We tend to plan proforma – in the way of filling out a sheet by putting in our name, d.o.b. address, and so on – in compartments that divide our selves into units of varying length but units nevertheless – units that have a start and an end as do the clearly-defined minute, hour, day, month, undergrad course, span from cradle to grave. It is how we are. How we speak. Words have an end. Their noises and meanings stop and start. But existence is an analogue. All the while we move from one compartment to the next are there sub-atomic particles trembling in and out of being, multitudes of microbes seething restlessly, blood cells coursing through our veins, thoughts streaming through our subconscious minds as we sleep and shower and eat – thoughts that we aren't even aware we've had – giving rise to rogue feelings that bob to the surface out of nowhere – sudden optimism – gladly-received but apparently groundless – then gathering storm clouds on our mind's horizon that bring a dread sense of impending doom even though there ought (apparently) to be no reason for concern. This is the human condition – in some cases more melancholic than others – so really, when it comes to 'best laid plans', none of us ever stood a chance.

Even if one were blessed to be healthy, happy, generous, kind and considerate in nature, and have innate ability coupled with the greatest self-control and motivation to succeed, first at school and college, and then in work and in play and marriage – life in general – would there always be those less fortunate to live alongside, people with all their 'imperfections' – 'ordinary' people! And if one were truly empathetic then, inevitably, this difference in potential would itself lead to personal stress as one worried about doing something to help – to alleviate suffering, to improve the lot of others less fortunate. And if one chose instead to cut oneself off – perhaps having the means to live a 'charmed life' – well, then that would be to live in solitude and no doubt unhappily – because we need other people. In any case, the mind of the recluse is far from perfect.

'No, no,' he thought to himself, as he worked. 'Take the tuning of this piano. If the strings were tuned to perfect mathematical thirds, the music played would sound wrong to our ears. In fact that is how it used to be, but if an instrument is tuned that way now, it sounds dreadful! Music played in some keys produces dissonant harmonics known as 'wolf notes'. That was how the well-tempered tuning came about – as a kind of 'compromise' that makes the intervals of pitch the same in all keys. So was Bach's 24 preludes and fugues of 'The Well-Tempered Clavier' devised to 'test' this system of tuning, running as it does through each and every key with a pair of major and minor compositions. It is the work of the tuner of a modern piano to temper the tuning by slightly sharpening some intervals and flattening others to bring about an harmonious whole, and so it is with the human psyche which is necessarily imperfect. Put simply, we have to live with our imperfections, work round them, embrace them even, so that they become a positive part of our whole.'

He continued on this train of thought of the pianoforte and its construction and operation serving as a metaphor for the human psyche. 'Take the cast iron frame of a piano – under constant and considerable stress – the frame of your average upright takes a load of several tons – is designed to take it and in most cases can withstand it. Sometimes a frame warps or cracks under the strain, but mostly they do not, and from all of that pent-up, potentially destructive energy, comes harmony.'

It was late one Friday afternoon shortly before Christmas, when Fairbright was sitting at the old upright playing Beethoven's Moonlight Sonata – a piece that his mother had particularly liked and sometimes played herself – that there'd come a soft knock at the door – so soft, in fact, that at first he'd carried on playing. Only when it came again no louder, did he stop and go over to open the door and find standing there a small, physically unprepossesing man with a round, mild-mannered face. He was holding a briefcase and smiling. His name was Hunter and, as Fairbright discovered, his handshake was as limp as one can get, so that the passage of energy in greeting him was all one way.

Fairbright assumed he was some kind of speculative cold-caller come about improvements – for he was well aware that the woodwork of the door and window frames was sorely in need of attention and that his house did to some extent 'let down' others in the mews. But it became clear that the lie of the land was entirely the other way as Hunter produced a document which seemed to show that the company for whom he worked as its sole employee and owner had – under conditions where maintenance payments had lapsed – a legal entitlement over the house.

He saw with perhaps greater clarity than he had ever seen anything before in his life, that the outstanding amount of £20,000 was one he couldn't possibly meet, and that if he did not, he would, according to the terms, lose his home. Hunter continued to smile as he apologised for bearing bad news, before placing a copy of the document gently into Fairbright's hand and bidding him 'good day'. Peter Fairbright watched as the small stranger who had just turned his life on its head, diminished down the darkening mews before vanishing on to the London streets.

The family solicitors confirmed that from a legal standpoint the document was watertight, and went a step further on their client's behalf by checking Hunter's status. They had it on good authority that not only was he expert in this business of resurrecting lapsed legal arrangements as life might be breathed into corpses, but absolutely ruthless – a formidable adversary for anyone who might try to stand up to him. Not for the last time did Fairbright spend his evening into the early hours racking his brains for a way out.

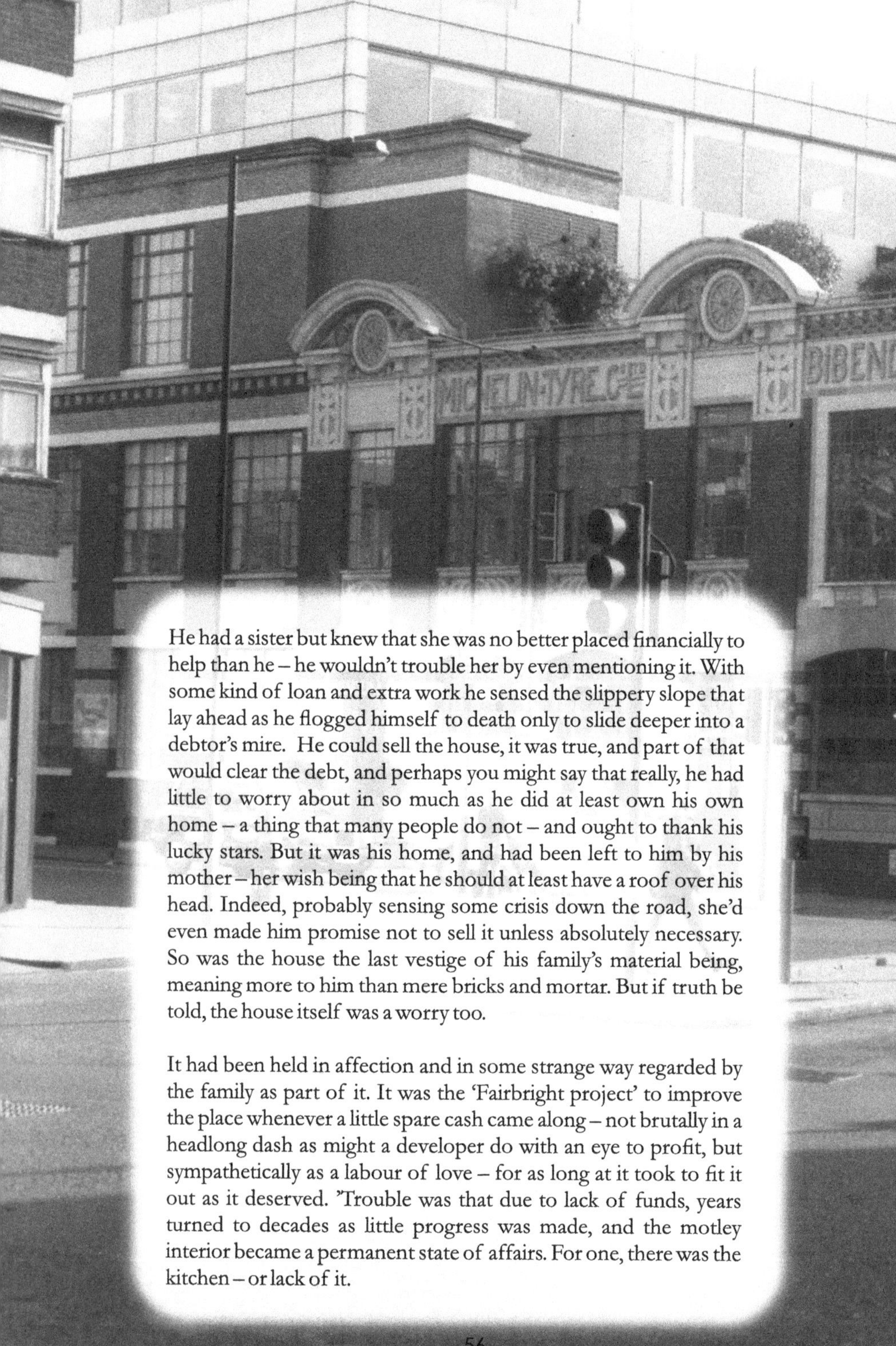

He had a sister but knew that she was no better placed financially to help than he – he wouldn't trouble her by even mentioning it. With some kind of loan and extra work he sensed the slippery slope that lay ahead as he flogged himself to death only to slide deeper into a debtor's mire. He could sell the house, it was true, and part of that would clear the debt, and perhaps you might say that really, he had little to worry about in so much as he did at least own his own home – a thing that many people do not – and ought to thank his lucky stars. But it was his home, and had been left to him by his mother – her wish being that he should at least have a roof over his head. Indeed, probably sensing some crisis down the road, she'd even made him promise not to sell it unless absolutely necessary. So was the house the last vestige of his family's material being, meaning more to him than mere bricks and mortar. But if truth be told, the house itself was a worry too.

It had been held in affection and in some strange way regarded by the family as part of it. It was the 'Fairbright project' to improve the place whenever a little spare cash came along – not brutally in a headlong dash as might a developer do with an eye to profit, but sympathetically as a labour of love – for as long at it took to fit it out as it deserved. 'Trouble was that due to lack of funds, years turned to decades as little progress was made, and the motley interior became a permanent state of affairs. For one, there was the kitchen – or lack of it.

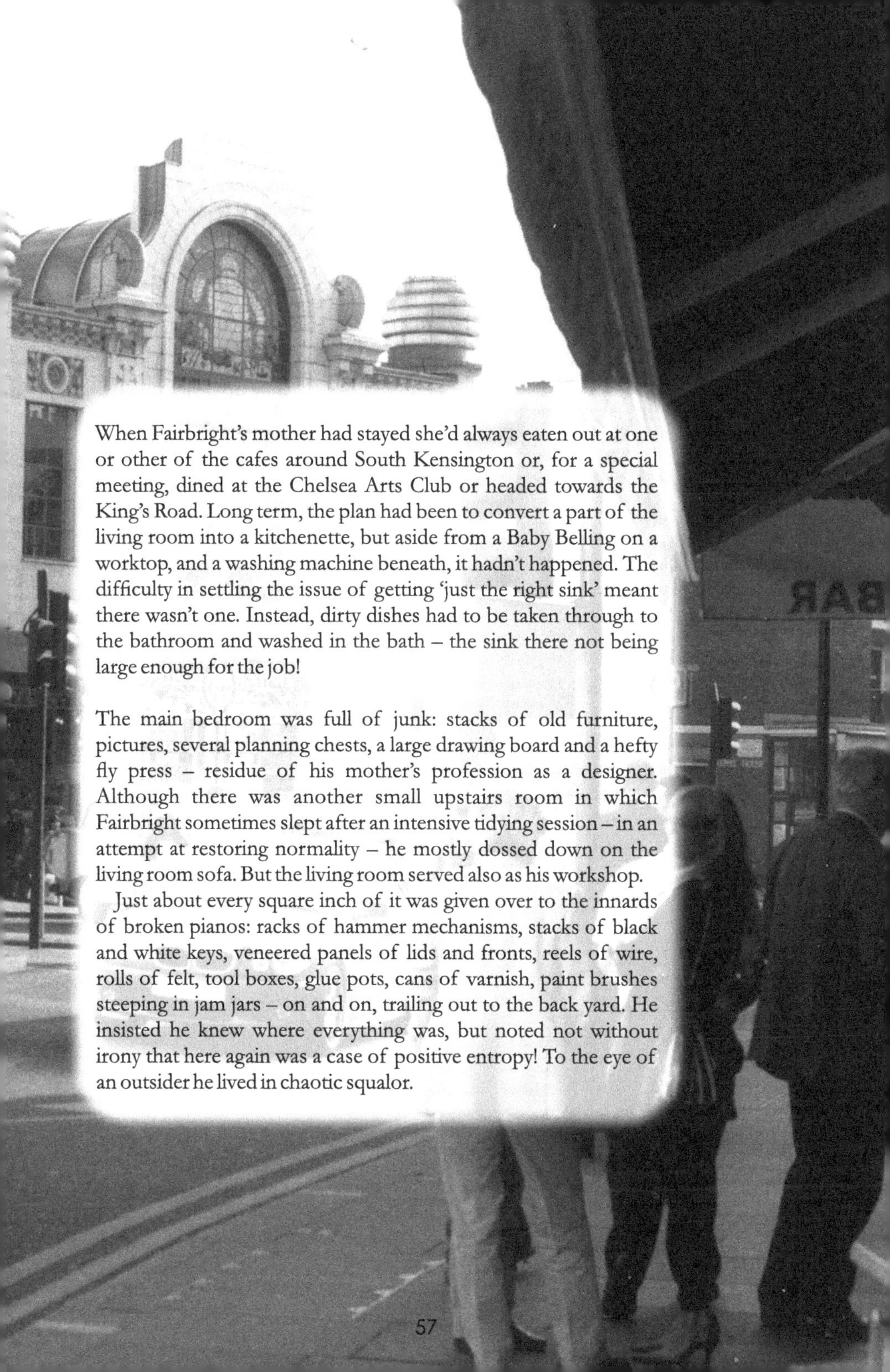

When Fairbright's mother had stayed she'd always eaten out at one or other of the cafes around South Kensington or, for a special meeting, dined at the Chelsea Arts Club or headed towards the King's Road. Long term, the plan had been to convert a part of the living room into a kitchenette, but aside from a Baby Belling on a worktop, and a washing machine beneath, it hadn't happened. The difficulty in settling the issue of getting 'just the right sink' meant there wasn't one. Instead, dirty dishes had to be taken through to the bathroom and washed in the bath – the sink there not being large enough for the job!

The main bedroom was full of junk: stacks of old furniture, pictures, several planning chests, a large drawing board and a hefty fly press – residue of his mother's profession as a designer. Although there was another small upstairs room in which Fairbright sometimes slept after an intensive tidying session – in an attempt at restoring normality – he mostly dossed down on the living room sofa. But the living room served also as his workshop.

Just about every square inch of it was given over to the innards of broken pianos: racks of hammer mechanisms, stacks of black and white keys, veneered panels of lids and fronts, reels of wire, rolls of felt, tool boxes, glue pots, cans of varnish, paint brushes steeping in jam jars – on and on, trailing out to the back yard. He insisted he knew where everything was, but noted not without irony that here again was a case of positive entropy! To the eye of an outsider he lived in chaotic squalor.

So had he thrown himself into his work, taking on as much as he could manage and more, increasingly neglecting his own welfare to bury his mind deep enough for it not to return to thoughts of Hunter, debt and what might be done. But the problem remained and a month into the New Year, one afternoon when there had been a steady fall of snow – enough to settle and deaden even the sound of traffic from the nearby Cromwell Road (something he could not remember happening in all the time he'd been there) there came again the soft knock. Now there was nothing for it but to fall on Hunter's mercy and appeal to his sense of decency in the hope that he might at least grant more time.

The meeting did not go well. Hunter advised him that if he didn't clear his debt or make some significant provision to immediately, he'd have no choice but to set legal wheels in motion and settle in court – inevitably leaving Fairbright ruined and homeless. Perhaps it was the way in which Hunter had sat and looked over the impressive clutter while holding the mug of tea Fairbright had made for him, and said (smiling as he did) that he couldn't see any good reason why a person oughtn't to jump at a chance of being shot of such a place, that had hurt most of all. It wasn't even a jibe – the man seemed to have no sensibility towards the power of material objects and spaces to touch people's lives, no shred of compassion.

The meeting left Fairbright dismayed, desperate, angry – angry towards this man who made his living by unerring predatory instinct and who was about to profit from something to which, morally at least, he had no right. Resentful and besieged, a few minutes later had Fairbright throttling his antagonist, dismembering him, carefully wrapping his remains in plastic sheeting and jamming them inside a Broadwood which with a Herculean effort he loaded into the back of his van, drove in the dead of night to a remote south-coast quayside, before releasing it into the English Channel – or would have, if murder didn't put him a rung or two lower on the ladder of despicability than Hunter himself! Anyway, he didn't have the stomach for it.

Resolving next day to start tidying the house top to bottom – at least to get his material affairs in order – he made his way ploddingly upstairs to the backroom in which he occasionally slept, and lay down.

It was in the dead of night as he hovered between waking and sleeping, walking through some other-wordly dream, searching and searching as it seemed for something that had so far eluded him, that he heard the sound of a piano being played: a faint cascade of notes of uncertain pitch that seemed to tumble from the dream. He opened his eyes and came awake to what was, quite unmistakeably, the sound of a single note dying away from the old piano downstairs. He swallowed hard and looked about the room that seemed to him as in a painting – part in deep shadow of midnight blue, its remainder bathed in the opalescent light of the moon. Swinging his legs over the bed and on to the floor, he felt there the grain of wood under his feet. He slid his arms into his dressing gown, pulling it round him as he crept softly to the top of the stairs, from where he listened, straining for the sound of movement – some creak from the room below. Hearing nothing he called down in a bold voice: 'Who's there?' The silence that returned was absolute. He put out a hand for the switch which came under his fingers as light filled the stairwell. Then did he glide down the stairway and steal quietly into the living room, from where he looked to the corner to see at the old piano a woman sitting motionless with her back to him. He stood a moment in wonder and mouthed the word: "Mother". But no sound came. Even as he tried again to project that word from his lips did he see the head turn to reveal a cheek and features that were not his mother's but those of another – formless with the indent of a smiling mouth. He cried out and jumped awake to find himself still in bed, shaking, cold and soaked in sweat.

Next morning, after making himself breakfast and resolving to take more care of himself to protect his sanity at least, he sat a while on the sofa, gathering himself for the undertaking ahead. He'd have to be ruthless. If he started looking at every item and reading every scrap, it'd take forever – he'd be sunk.

Much of the stuff hadn't been touched since his mother's passing. Every bundle of postcards held by a band became a trap as he was torn between dropping them without a second thought into the rubbish sack or removing the band to look. Of course he had looked, and riffled quickly through them, seeing that some had been sent by relatives but mostly friends on their holidays – he hadn't realized she'd so many. There were birthday cards he and his sister had made for her when they were little – drawings of animals, flowers and words of love in big wobbly letters. 'Just cards and paper,' he thought, turning them and holding them crosswise, about to tear them through. He hesitated and placed these also to one side. It was as if, through these things, one generation was talking to another and if he didn't hear his mother's voice, he fancied her words came to him: 'Take the time to look – or what does any of it matter?'

One of the few letters he'd sent to her, written in happier times was here. She must have thought a lot of it to bother keeping it. He read it through. He felt glad he'd written it – glad he'd taken the time to tell her what he'd thought. What a different person he'd been – so full of optimism! There was a green paper napkin with the printed motif of a restaurant where they'd eaten when she'd come to visit him. He picked up a book which fell open at a mark which he saw carried a quotation from a psalm: 'For he will command his angels concerning you, to guard you in all your ways.' He put the bookmark into his pocket.

In one room was a large leather suitcase held with a strap. This he unbuckled. He lifted the lid. It was full of shoeboxes each jammed full of photos – hundreds and hundreds – many black and white. From one, a young man looked out at him – slightly built, with lots of black hair – smiling, white teeth – a young man who looked as if he might do anything – so different from the image he carried in his mind's eye – portly, hair greying – the disappointed man his father had become. Here was his mother holding his baby sister in her arms – barely able to contain her delight, and here he was in his pram fat in the face, brimming effusively with joy.

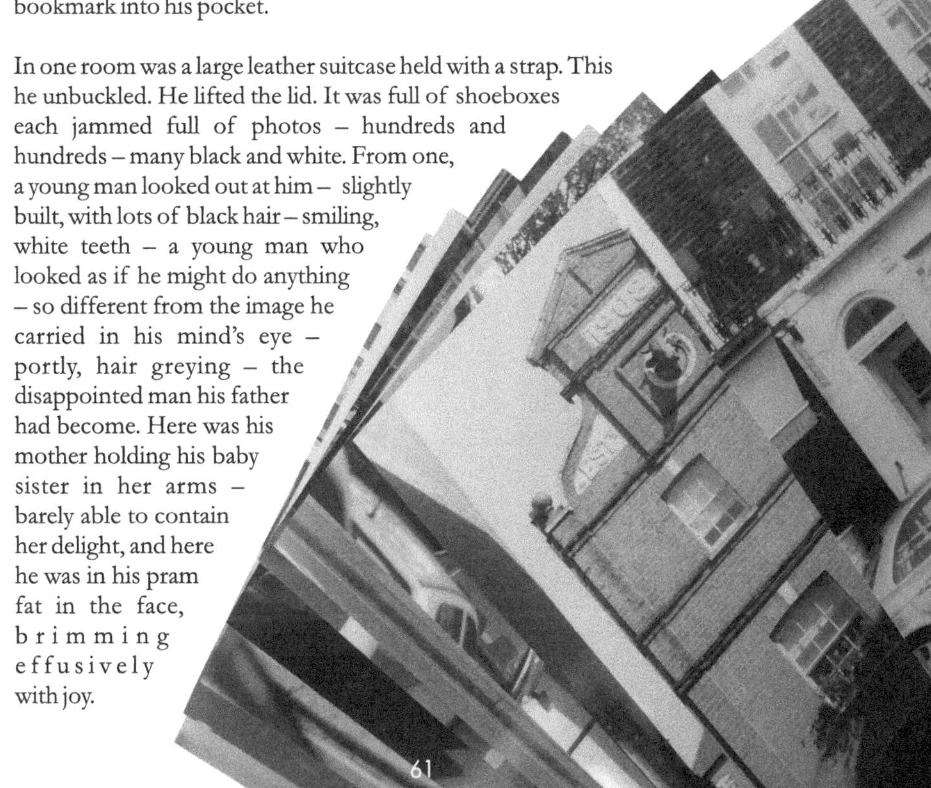

There were so many he couldn't even begin to start looking – and shouldn't! A sudden impulse came upon him to tear up the photos in an irrevocable move to nullify all this 'stuff'. 'Just pictures,' he thought. 'Paper – not people, nor the souls of people! He wouldn't be destroying the past – none of it could bring his parents back – it was absurd!' But he found he could not. Carefully, he placed the photos back in their boxes, fastened up the case and let it be.

So as he made his way through each room there grew a pile of things which he must take with him – wherever that was to be – that might be sorted through when there was more time. Though he knew quite well there never would be.

It took the best part of a week to get through the house top to bottom, and though at the end was there far less stuff and what there was was at least stacked neatly on swept floors, there was still a lot. He'd made the most impact on the living room, banishing much of the piano detritus so now he enjoyed a clear living space. He'd even cleaned the windows through which there came wintry sunlight that penetrated to the farthest corners. In one of these stood the old Chappell piano that had been there since the day his mother had moved in. This he was inclined to ignore until the time came to move and either pass it on with the house – as had the previous owner – or just dump it. He remembered the times his mother had sat and played it, and the words came to him again: 'Take the time to look – or what does any of it matter?'

Though he'd tuned it he'd never cleaned it or otherwise touched it, apart from to play it occasionally. He lifted the lid over the keys and plunked on the bass octave, then peered into its dusty interior – if he gave it some attention he might be able to get a bit for it. He removed the front panel and then the lid over the keys and leaned them against the wall. Then he removed the bottom panel and as he did so saw in its base a dirty canvas bag. He lifted it out – it was heavy. He took it to the table, where he loosened its drawstring and opened it. Inside was a dull metallic rock which he placed on the table – a dense, dark brown thing that was mostly smooth except for one side where part had broken away to reveal the granular interior. Stone? Metal? What was it?

He assumed it had been put inside the piano for safe-keeping and yet it appeared to be nothing of any value – it was mystifying. Perhaps a geologist at the nearby college of mining might shed some light on it? He'd take it over when he had a spare moment.

In fact, so little did the rock's appearance impress Fairbright that it lay on the table for a further week before finally he got around to taking it – not to the college of mining, but to the museum of natural history. After some waiting at the main desk there'd appeared a wiry, bearded gent in a dun-coloured jacket – a researcher attached to the Department of Mineralogy – who introduced him self simply as 'Scruton'.

Scruton led him down to his basement office – a small, dingy room lined with wooden chests of drawers and glass-fronted cabinets filled with mineral specimens. Some were cut and polished and there seemed to be every conceivable colour and pattern under the sun. Fairbright guessed some of these were rare and precious – probably worth a great deal of money – a far cry from his own 'find'. He took the rock from the bag and placed it on the desk in front of Scruton who sat there with his arms folded, leaning over it. He asked Fairbright where he'd found it. Just for a second was he tempted to be evasive but checked himself and told the truth.

The expert put a loupe to his eye and examined the rock closely. Fairbright watched his concentrated expression for some response but still there came no discernible reaction one way or another – either the man hadn't a clue what he was looking at or, if he did, would have made an admirable poker player.

'I'm pretty sure it's not of this Earth,' he began finally, 'but to be certain we'd have to run some tests – that's if you were to agree to it. But I should warn you – things don't move quickly here – you might have to wait a while for the results.' Fairbright agreed, and after some intensive form-filling and returning again to provide his driving licence as ID, took away a 'chit' signed by Scruton in return for the museum's loan of his rock.

In the two months that he waited for a reply, he put the mews house with an estate agent, setting the price low, resolving to settle the debt and move out of London – preferably as far away as he could get from the rogues of this city! Not surprisingly, there'd been plenty of interest, and now there were several offers to consider. At the same time there arrived a letter from the museum on headed paper saying simply that the results of the tests were in and that if he'd like to arrange to drop by, he (Scruton) would run through them with him when he came to collect his property.

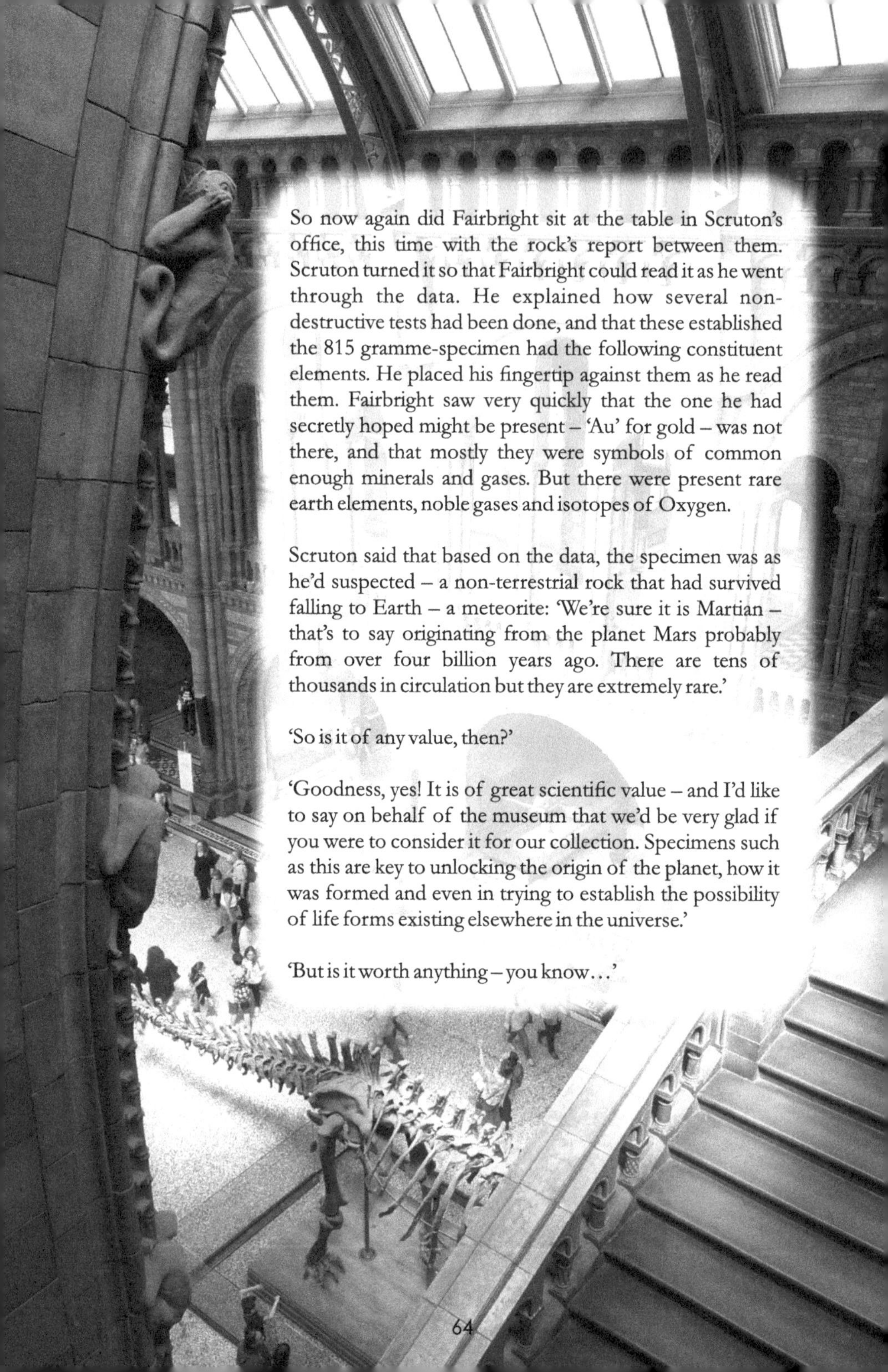

So now again did Fairbright sit at the table in Scruton's office, this time with the rock's report between them. Scruton turned it so that Fairbright could read it as he went through the data. He explained how several non-destructive tests had been done, and that these established the 815 gramme-specimen had the following constituent elements. He placed his fingertip against them as he read them. Fairbright saw very quickly that the one he had secretly hoped might be present – 'Au' for gold – was not there, and that mostly they were symbols of common enough minerals and gases. But there were present rare earth elements, noble gases and isotopes of Oxygen.

Scruton said that based on the data, the specimen was as he'd suspected – a non-terrestrial rock that had survived falling to Earth – a meteorite: 'We're sure it is Martian – that's to say originating from the planet Mars probably from over four billion years ago. There are tens of thousands in circulation but they are extremely rare.'

'So is it of any value, then?'

'Goodness, yes! It is of great scientific value – and I'd like to say on behalf of the museum that we'd be very glad if you were to consider it for our collection. Specimens such as this are key to unlocking the origin of the planet, how it was formed and even in trying to establish the possibility of life forms existing elsewhere in the universe.'

'But is it worth anything – you know…'

'Oh... oh, I see! You mean is it of any monetary value? Well, er... I can only speak from the point of view of a scientist rather than a collector or dealer, you understand. As with anything, it's what people will pay. The weight, rarity, physical appearance, narrative attached and provenance can all affect the monetary value of a specimen. Ones that were witnessed to actually fall or that have some kind of interesting story attached can go for a fair bit. The Beaver L5 chondrite was used as a doorstop in a US county gaol for many years before someone realized what it was. Not so long ago Claxton L5 destroyed a post box in Georgia. These are now legendary. Pieces from some of the more prevalent specimens can be picked up for less than one pound sterling per gramme, I believe. Of course, the one you have here is much rarer…'

'Not exactly worth its weight in gold, then?'

'Goodness, no no!' said Scruton, laughing and taking off his glasses to clean them. 'I'd say, worth perhaps… hmm… 5... 10 times its weight in gold – maybe more. I wonder how on earth it ended up in your piano?'

April 2020

Flood Street

Dust reconstituted
With water
A place where sensations meet
A bunch of memories
Like the Rough Trade record
Tappity-tap on the drums
Like when she kissed him
And pushed his lips hard
Against his teeth
Tappity-tap on the drums,
And he saw her with him
And the jealousy was like
A rubber tummy
Tappity-tap
Jeans drum-skin tight
His fingers on her

And the air was like
Green Park in spring
High cheek bones
Skin blushing
Piled-hair glistening,
Bursting with animal life
Too much for anyone
All animal
Intense love, sweet enough for Jesus
And tears of joy
Dripping like rain from leaves
Tappity-tap
Summer smell of limes
Transparent green
Bright future promised
In a Chelsea back street
Under London Planes in Autumn
And the smell of warm dust
When the first drops of rain hit
Tappity-tap, winter coming
Memories and sensations
Just dust
Reconstituted.

March 2018

Palimpsest

No *tabula rasa*,
Each new page comes
With half-remembered
Thoughts and pictures
Showing through.

Forgotten now as you write,
There lies in a box a print,
Made 30 years ago,
Of a couple passing
Over a London bridge,
Taken in,
In the blink of eye
And shuttered lens.
And here now,
The same in text.

'Every spread
Must carry an image' –
Publisher's rule –
Followed by this fool!
So do I delve through
Hundreds there,
In search of one to fit –
Laterally, perhaps, as metaphor,
Or wholly abstractedly –
By delightful obscurity, (you wish)!
But not literally –
Unless...

Unless – it was one taken in...
In the blink of eye
And shuttered lens,
Here now,
In this box
As in text –
Page and mind as one,
As palimpsest.

June 2020

Fall

"A river puts you right in touch with nature," said Travis as he peeled potatoes into a carrier bag. "At night you feel the tide rise under you, hear her straining at the mooring – don't even need to pull the curtains. You can look out from where you lie and see the stars. In the morning there's the river stretching upstream – your back garden! And all the while you are right on the edge of the city. It's the only way to live!"

"What if you sink?" said Alice, sipping at her mug of coffee and eyeing him shrewdly from beneath her fringe.

"Well, there is always that. But you just have to try to keep on top of things."

"Like the water."

"Like the water. Anyway, hull on this thing's about a centimetre thick and bullet proof."

"Doesn't it rust?"

"Rusts a bit then stops – gets a coating of iron oxide. Won't go no more."

"You hope!"

"Anyway, there's anti-fouling paint – has to be done every few years."

"How do you wash – you haven't a sink?"

"Very infrequently. Heat three of them big pots on the Calor gas – no more'n 10 minutes each, else it cools down before you start, and do the best you can. Still freezing, mind."

"What d'you use – not river water?"

"Well, you ain't gonna use drinking water, are you? I have to go all the way up to Eel Pie Island on me bike and trailer to fill that barrel – and it's heavy! Besides, river's a lot cleaner'un it used to be. There's salmon now – all sorts – otters, loads of herons and eels – herons eat the eels. There's even parakeets – green things – you've probably heard them – strident beggars!"

"You make it sound like the Amazon or something. I'm still not moving in with you."

"What's matter – too good for life on houseboat?"

“No. Of course not. It’s just that… well, where would I put all my stuff – my clothes and things? I like my own space. I might look a bit scruffy now, but that’s because I’m with you.”

“What – you saying I’m a tramp or something?”

“No. Just a bit… crusty.”

“Oh, crusty am I?”

Alice burst out laughing as Travis grabbed her round the waist, lifted her off the floor and swung her about playfully. They’d met at a festival some months before and were now lovers and steady partners. He’d asked her once before if she’d like to move on to the boat, but she’d been reluctant. He hadn’t broached the subject again.

Travis: “Those spuds are just about ready – I’ll mash ’em. There’s some sausages already done. Why don’t you open that bottle of wine? It’s cheap one from the offy up the top – but not all bad.

“There’s a nice cabin at the back,” he said, as they sat and ate, “full of junk but I could clear it. To be honest it’s the best room on here – being only me, just never got round to it. We could do it up for you. I was joking about the washing – you can use the showers at the swimming baths.”

“Well, I’d have to think about it. I suppose I could ride my bike along the river to work.”

“Some do. Take longer-un you think, though. If you took the loops out, wouldn’t be so bad. But that river don’t half meander. Reckon it’s about 8 miles to your hospital. Better to take the Tube. Cycling get you fit, mind.”

“Are you saying I’m fat?”

“What? Look at you – there’s not a pick on you! Need feeding up with a few more of these – want some?”

“No thanks. I’m stuffed. But I’ll have another glass of wine since you’re offering.”

So Alice agreed to move in.

"What d'you reckon," said Alice, holding up two large and very old looking cans of paint. "'Willow Green' or 'Dragon's Blood'?"

"Dunno – it's your room – you choose. Be surprised if any of 'em's any good – came with the boat."

Alice prised up a lid on one of the tins: "Hmm... that's solid. Look's like it's going to have to be..." She lifted the second lid, "Willow Green." "Thank goodness for that!" said Travis, laughing, "We don't want it looking like a blood bath!"

"Who does it belong to?" said Alice, as she carefully brushed out the paint.

"My parents' friends. I houseboat-sit for 'em in return for free rent. Never come here, mind – spend all their time in Holland. Dunno why they don't just sell it."

"They'd get nothing for it. Be honest, Travis – it's little better than a floating squat. They ought to be paying you to live here!"

"It could be done up. So long as hull's sound, don't matter – rest just sits on top. Anyway, you'd be surprised. It's the location that counts. Someone did up a public toilets not so far from here. Worth millions now. People give an arm and a leg to be in West London – riverside residence, 'n'all!"

"You make it sound like 'Toad Hall'!"

"No honestly, it'd make a lovely gaff. I'd put an offer in myself if I had anything to offer. But a few tins of paint don't cost anything. Some timbers need replacing – I'll get round to that. Mind you, better not turn it into a floating palace. Someone might start getting ideas!"

"I don't think you need to worry about that. But keep it shabby-chic, eh, just to be on the safe side!"

"Shabby-chic's right! Anyway, it's too nice to be stuck in. After we've got this coat on, what say we go to the park – you can bring your guitar. I love it when you sing for me."

" Huh! Who says I do it for you?"

They were sitting on a blanket in the long grass away from the footpaths that cross the wide expanse of the park. Alice was tearing off a part of a Rizla packet while Travis leaned back on his elbows looking about.

"Some of these oaks go back to Henry VIII's time – used to be his stomping ground when he was up at Hampton Court." He shielded his eyes from the sun and craned his neck forwards: "I can see him there now, look!"

"Who?" said Alice looking up, concerned.

"Henry and his hunting party, chasing a stag under those chestnut trees!"

"You idiot. I thought there was someone there."

Alice blew out the smoke and handed him the joint, which he pulled on and then after exhaling a cloud on to the sky said: "Seriously though, funny thing time and space. But for the jets you could be in Tudor England, medieval – anytime – planes put you here and now. I remember, I was on the boat watching Wimbledon on a little TV, and all you could hear was the sound of the ball going back and forth – 'pock', 'pock', 'pock' – then a plane goes over."

"What, on the telly?"

"On the telly. A minute later you'd hear it going over the boat – same one."

"How d'you know it was the same one?"

"Well, they keep going over pretty regular but then there'll be a gap – and for sure it's just the same on the boat. Kind of connecting you with all the millions watching all over the world – like an affirmation of time and place – that you're here and now. But that's just one type of time. Then there's – I dunno – 'head time' s'ppose you'd call it. That's different."

"Head time."

"Yeah."

"Hard to explain but see, I reckon we got time all wrong. Way we think we're on a line going forwards, past stretching back behind us, nosing into the future. But you say: 'Where is the present?' And you say: 'Here – now! Now! and now! Soon as you say it, it's gone – can't pin it! There ain't no 'now'. Goin' into the future at one second per second – it don't make any sense! I reckon time goes all ways and that we can travel in our minds – not just thinking about the past or the future, but somehow actually connecting with it – really going back, sinking way back – sideways, even. When you return, you feel the jolt – tells you you been somewhere."

"It's called 'daydreaming', Travis. You should have been a philosopher. Anyway, I know I have somewhere to go tomorrow – work – that's my future. But I've got a gig at *The Marlborough* on Wednesday. So that's something to look forward to."

"Got any new material?"

"I've written one new song. Shall I play it for you? You can tell me what you think."

Travis lay back with his arms folded over his chest and listened as Alice played. When she'd finished, he said: "D'you know, that was absolutely brilliant – lovely – you're wasted in that hospital – you should be filling stadiums, Alice."

"Steady!"

"No honestly, you got a brilliant voice – I could be your manager!"

"Travis, you can barely manage yourself, let alone anyone else. Anyway, I like my job. What have you got on this week?"

"Huh! Helping some guy with his boat up Teddington – some media producer arsehole – he's loaded but he 'a'n't got a clue – bloody perfectionist, mind. That should bring in a bit. There might be something at Isleworth. Apart from that, do what I can on ours, I expect."

A little while later, Alice suddenly became very serious and sat up. "Travis look," she said, pointing over his shoulder. "What's that?"

Travis turned and they both watched as it fell.

Travis was reluctant to have anything to do with authority and particularly the police, but as they walked back they decided they ought to report it. So Travis made a call from a payphone at a nearby pub and they went back to the park, where they were to be interviewed. They agreed Alice should do the talking.

"Where were you when you saw it?" said the police officer with a notebook.

"Just about here – there, you can see where the grass is flattened," said Alice.

The policeman glanced at the spot where they'd been sitting. "What did you see, exactly?"

"Well, I saw this thing falling and pointed it out to Travis. Over those trees." Alice pointed. "It was black – like a silhouette against the sky – a long way off – small. It sort of came down – not dead straight but going slightly to one side. Seemed to fall quite slowly. We both watched until it disappeared behind the trees."

"What shape was it?"

"You couldn't tell. It was too small."

"Where d'you think it came from?"

"Well, we didn't see it come from a plane. But one had just gone over. It was just after that we saw it. We assumed it came from the plane."

Travis chipped in: "We thought we'd better tell the police in case someone finds something in their garden and gets a nasty shock."

"What do you think it was, sir?"

"It could have been a body. But you couldn't see any arms or legs Well, I know there have been several cases – people desperate to get away from their country stowing away in the undercarriage just before take off. But at that altitude they become unconscious and usually just freeze to death. Body falls out when the undercarriage comes down – about where we saw it, I guess."

The police officer wrote down a few details in his notebook and then wandered off a little into the distance and got on to his radio. After a short while he returned and said he'd drop them both back in town. They thanked him and said they'd walk.

They were sitting at a little table on the houseboat with a copy of a local newspaper in front of them.

"Here we are," said Alice, turning over the page. She read from the paper: "Flights into Heathrow were diverted so that the police could conduct a helicopter search of the area around the gasworks when two local residents said they'd spotted what they thought was a body falling from a plane...' That's rubbish," said Alice indignantly. "We didn't even say that!"

"That's the press for you, all over!" said Travis.

"How did they get hold of it – the police wouldn't have told them, would they?"

"Dunno, maybe. Perhaps someone at the pub we phoned from or, er... that media bloke I'm working for – I told him."

"Oh Travis! Why did you do that? If the police don't find anything, people will think we're attention-seekers! We'll look like right idiots."

"Well, it's been playing on my mind. I thought they'd have found something by now – it's been 3 days. I assumed they'd tell us, if they did..."

"D'you still think it was a body?"

"I don't know."

"Perhaps it didn't come from the plane."

"Where else could it have come from? More likely the police didn't take us seriously and do a proper search."

"They put a up helicopter and diverted the planes. I'd say that was pretty serious."

"Yeh, but we just pointed to where we'd seen it – he didn't even take a photo or make a drawing. From that distance you only got to be a bit out and you'd be searching in completely the wrong place. He must have known we'd been smoking – I reckon he just thought we were unreliable – two stoned hippies."

"But if it had been a body, wouldn't a member of the public have found it by now – a dog walker or someone?"

"You'd have thought so. But we both saw something fall. It must have landed somewhere."

When Alice got back from work that evening Travis had a map open on the table and was marking various straight lines with a sharp pencil against a steel ruler.

"What are you doing?"

"I've been to the library and found some stuff on previous sightings and various things that have fallen from planes round here – several bodies, plane debris and lumps of dirty ice. I've got info about flight paths. I'm trying to work out where it might have landed."

"Well, I don't think it's healthy. It's becoming an obsession. I work in a hospital, I know about these things… And some of the people I work with have somehow got wind of the story – they've started to treat me differently."

"How d'you mean?"

"Well, they're a bit stand-offish and they aren't usually. One of them even said: ' What was it Andy Warhol said? '15 minutes of fame?'"

"Cheeky bugger!"

"Look Travis, if something's found – fine – we'll find out. If not, it'll just remain a mystery – that's okay with me. Let's just get on with out lives."

"Okay, sure – but I just want to try one thing. If I can work out roughly where it might have landed, and if it's somewhere I can access, I can go on my bike and take a look – I can do that much."

"Well, I think you're mad – you think you can find it on your bike when the police used a helicopter? It's like looking for a needle in a haystack. I'm going to practise my guitar for a bit."

Alice made herself a coffee and took it to her room and shut the door.

Travis felt the boat bump against the mooring posts as it rose with the tide. He could hear Alice playing her new song – just the guitar without the vocals. He looked at the map where he'd drawn a narrow sector whose point ended on Heathrow Airport and then, within that, another narrower one. He marked a point in the park where he reckoned they'd sat, and from it drew another narrow sector that he estimated crossed above the trees where they'd seen it fall. Then he hatched-in the area of the intersection and looked closely at what lay inside.

Travis pushed open the iron gates and wheeled his bike in. Then he leaned it against the wall and locked it. The irony of looking for 'his' corpse in a cemetery had not escaped him. Assuming that the grounds must be visited several times on a daily basis and tended closely by grounds staff, he'd started here by way of process of elimination, as it were, as being the least likely place where anything could fall without being found. He'd get it over quickly and move on to the more likely options. There was an office attached to the cemetery but it looked to be closed and, in any case, he thought it best not to involve other people as far as possible – explanations could prove awkward. Anyway, he wasn't sure what he was looking for.

Had the police been here? No chance. Could a helicopter even pick up a cold corpse lying dashed to earth as it would be from that height? Possibly, but he doubted they'd given it more than an hour. More likely they'd weighed up the likelihood of two 'weed-smoking losers' either being mistaken or making the whole thing up, over the disruption to one of the world's busiest air corridors for sufficient time to prove otherwise, and decided not to bother. Fair enough! He'd have a proper look.

He'd reasoned that a thing might land anywhere – on a roof, in a garden, on a road or pavement, in a car park or even on a car – all places where people would come across it, and hadn't. Forget the habitations (he'd thought) there might just be a chance with the rest. But if there's a lot of concrete, brick and tarmac in a city, the remainder is vast – commons, parks, playing fields, golf courses, allotments and then all the bits in between – ground owned by utility and transport companies, local councils – borders alongside railway lines, dual carriageways and footpaths, between housing estates, alongside streams and rivers – neglected patches inaccessible to the public that might go decades without anyone setting foot there – the sorts of places you sometimes see from the window of a railway carriage – bramble-filled triangles between the intersections – little enclaves with small woods of silver birch and ponds even – acres of buddleia reclaiming 'ours' on 'Her' behalf – places about as wild as you'll get in a city where you can count on every square inch being combed and disputed over – motivated by self-interest if not greed.

A slab of ice, a corpse, a bag containing the riches of the world – whatever this thing was that had fallen could in all possibility have landed here, but as he walked the path between the stones and surveyed the rows of graves stretching into the vale before him, he realized it was impossible even to begin looking . Alice was right. It was vain. And in any case, he somehow knew that it would not be here.

He read one or two of the gravestones – some were names he recognized. He read some more – here lay actors and actresses, musicians and singers, artists, military commanders, politicians and the archeological explorers of ancient lands . All of these people had passed this same way. Here was time once again playing its tricks – the past stretching out before him as far as the eye could see all squeezed through this eye-of-a-needle moment, along with his own future.

Turning his back on the graves he walked back to his bike and unchained it. He decided not to bother with the Common or the Heath – the mystery would remain, but that was okay. He pedalled back through the park and free-wheeled most of the way downhill to the houseboat, where he found Alice getting ready for her gig.

"Find anything?" she asked, with a look of knowing amusement.

"Yes," he said, giving her a gentle hug, "just... not what I expected."

May 2020

Plinthed

She'd received a letter written
From the Arts Council of Great Britain
Commissioning artwork from her
For the Fourth Plinth.

Though she was delighted
She was more than slightly frighted
She hadn't started,
And she only had a month.

She met with Frannie Bacon
Whom in her, had he an interest taken,
Seeking Soho inspiration
At the French Pub.

They drank absinthe and Bolly
And got totally trollied
And not a little 'plinthed' too
At the Colony Club.

In nights of restless sleeplessness
Did she tap her deep subconsciousness,
Until inspiration flooded
From her fevered mind.

It was awfully pretentious,
Lewd and licentious,
A degenerate art idea,
Of the worst kind.

It was non-derivational,
Totally original,
Devoid of visual cliché,
Not a hackneyed phrase in sight.

It took a Phd to get it,
And the pundits applauded it,
She met with huge success
On her opening night.

If sloganned then subliminal,
It was pared-down minimal,
Worked on several layers
Had thirteen coats of paint.

But if the critics applauded it
The public were appalled by it:
'Just the King's New Clothes!' they shouted,
'Art it ain't.'

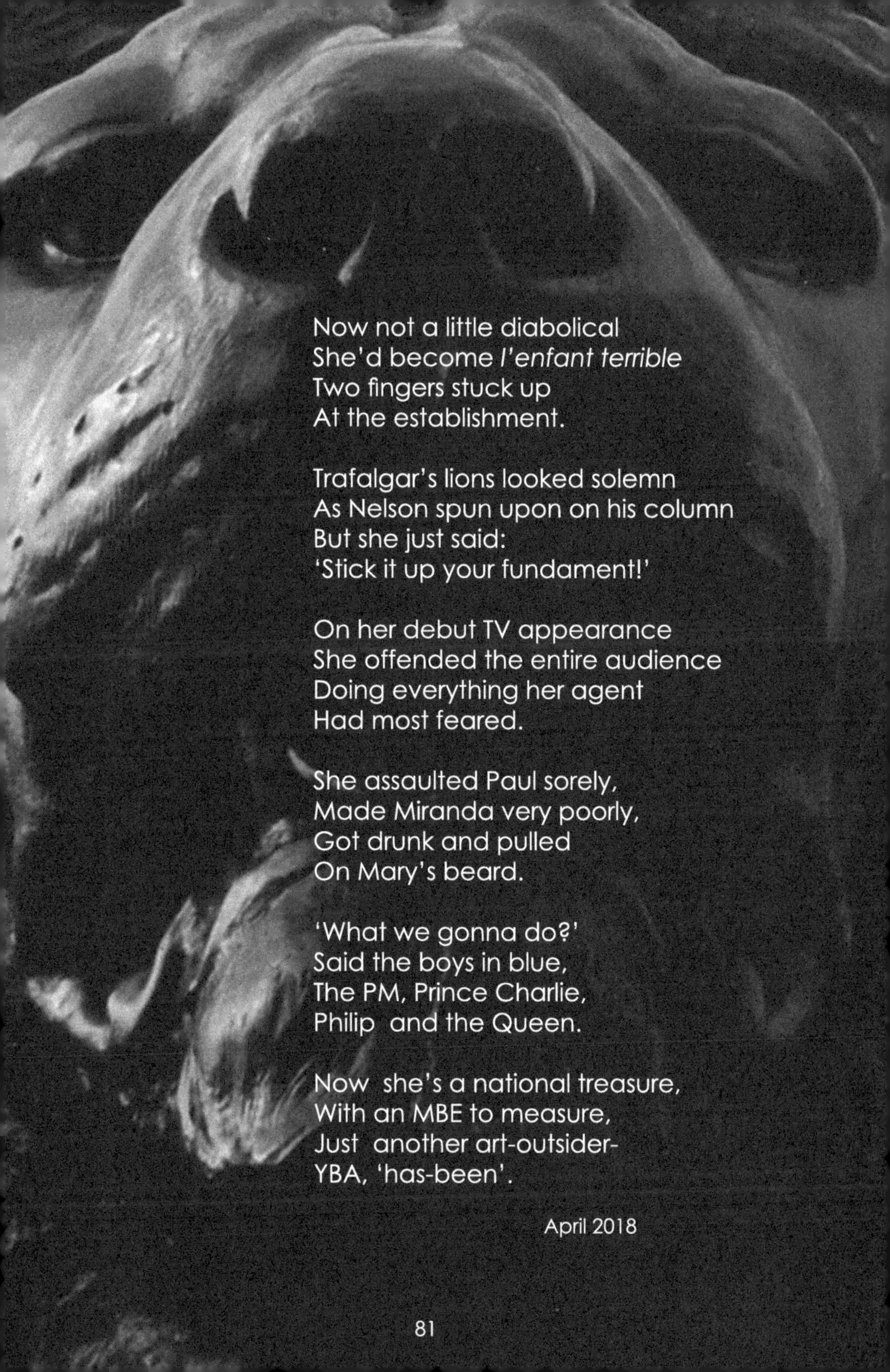

Now not a little diabolical
She'd become *l'enfant terrible*
Two fingers stuck up
At the establishment.

Trafalgar's lions looked solemn
As Nelson spun upon on his column
But she just said:
'Stick it up your fundament!'

On her debut TV appearance
She offended the entire audience
Doing everything her agent
Had most feared.

She assaulted Paul sorely,
Made Miranda very poorly,
Got drunk and pulled
On Mary's beard.

'What we gonna do?'
Said the boys in blue,
The PM, Prince Charlie,
Philip and the Queen.

Now she's a national treasure,
With an MBE to measure,
Just another art-outsider-
YBA, 'has-been'.

April 2018

English Country Stile

'X' marks the spot
Where two steps cross,
And an oaken stump
To lean upon
Breaks the hedge
Diagonally opposite –
Secret ways, that say:
'Come on!'

'X' marks the spot
Where, so they said,
A crossed witch flew
Upside-down upon a stick
To spite a farmer,
Souring his herd's milk,
Making cattle sick.

'X' marks the spot
Where a pagan queen
Stepped from her mount
To bury there a purse
Not so deep
Beneath our England
Guarded by a curse.

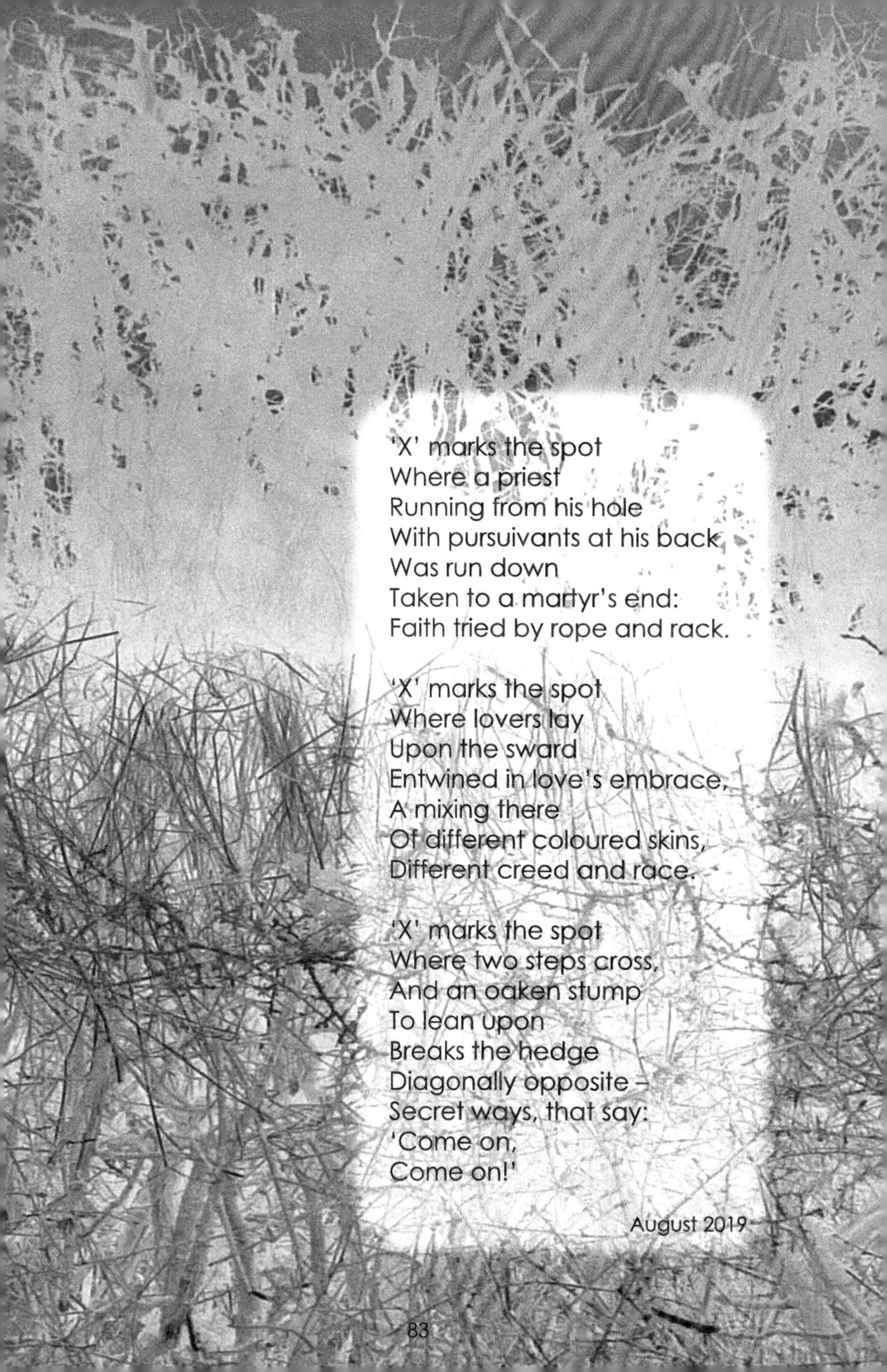

'X' marks the spot
Where a priest
Running from his hole
With pursuivants at his back
Was run down
Taken to a martyr's end:
Faith tried by rope and rack.

'X' marks the spot
Where lovers lay
Upon the sward
Entwined in love's embrace,
A mixing there
Of different coloured skins,
Different creed and race.

'X' marks the spot
Where two steps cross,
And an oaken stump
To lean upon
Breaks the hedge
Diagonally opposite –
Secret ways, that say:
'Come on,
Come on!'

August 2019

Digging

I saw him from the bridge –
The ancient bridge upon the pilgrim's way
To the holy Head
Marking 4 miles to go –
Digging there in the mud

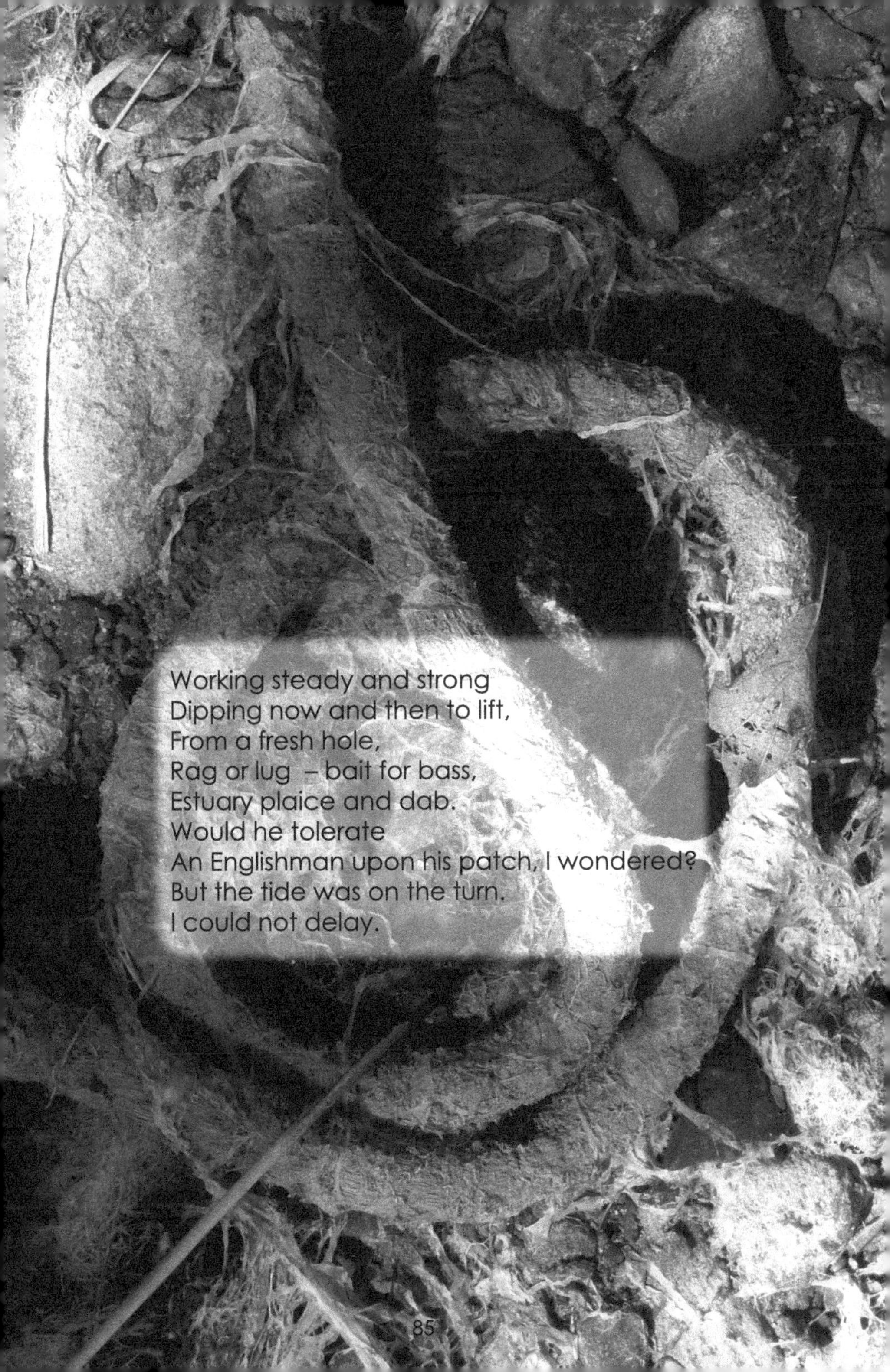

Working steady and strong
Dipping now and then to lift,
From a fresh hole,
Rag or lug – bait for bass,
Estuary plaice and dab.
Would he tolerate
An Englishman upon his patch, I wondered?
But the tide was on the turn.
I could not delay.

Hair blows across his face
As I approach.
Doesn't look up.
Knows I'm there.
Was that an oath uttered
Between a Curlew's cries?
Did I hear the wind
Carry away a curse?

Thrusts again that dreadful fork
With silver tines worn needle-sharp
Through years of work,
Through the crust of sea-grit, shells
And tiny crabs
Into the ooze beneath,
And lifts.

'Not too close,' I think.
I begin to dig.
Fork stumbles on hidden stones,
Locks fast as I lift,
There is a knack I do not have.
Just once do I see a red tail disappear
Before I can hold it –
Sand dragon gone.

4 holes fill with water
Nothing to show!
If my life depended on it,
I'd starve before the fishing began!
I've grown soft.
I break sweat.
I lean in and lift.
There is a thud.
Wood breaks
Above metal.

Ironmonger's new fork in hand
(More at home in a garden shed
Glowing, conspicuously, yellow!)
I return to see water lapping
At my footprints stretching ahead.
I've missed the tide.

Now he has the white tub
At the water's edge
Dipping it there
Swirling and swilling
Like a 49-er
Panning for gold,
Cleaning his find.

Then he takes up his great fork,
The likes of which I've never seen,
And strides across the mudflat towards me,
Brooding under long hair blowing,
Glowering, intoning, as it seems.
Closing on me purposefully.
I am a tourist. This is his living. His patch.

He smiles, showing teeth like tombstones.
'Saw you broke your fork,' he says –
Not mockingly as he might,
But sympathetically as one to another
Who knows.
Takes a generous handful from his bucket –
More than generous – puts it into mine,
'Just tails,' he says,
And walks on.

May 2019

The Rock Pool

There is a singularity to the way
It fills. Two or three
Small waves bring a murmur
Or gurgle only, then comes
A proper one, but funnelled in,
So the sound is like a hollow flush –
As of some mighty
Victorian lavatory cistern! –

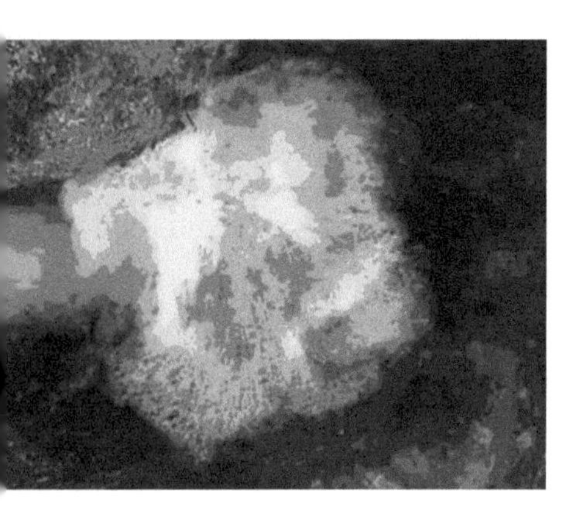

Pushing saltwater in at
The head of the pool
For a moment frothing –
Effervescent with clear bubbles –
Then stilling to a lovely deep green
As the new water is transmitted
Down the pool,
In a slow wave of tranquility.

Bit by bit does the level rise –
Imperceptibly,
Minute by minute –
So an hour later
You are surprised how high
It has come.

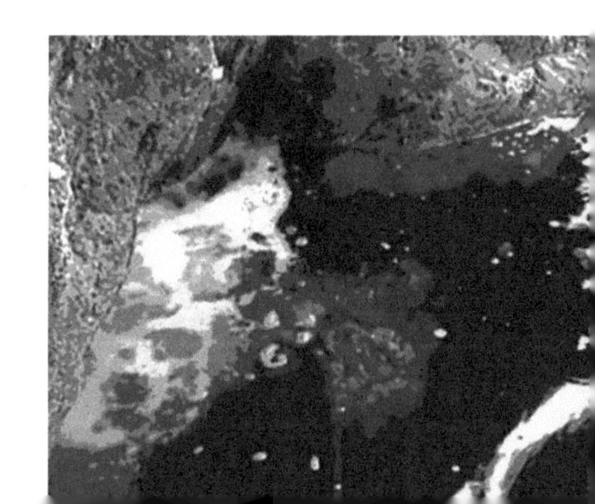

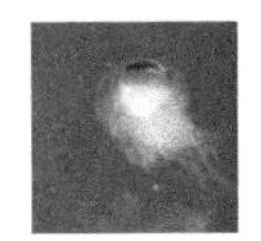
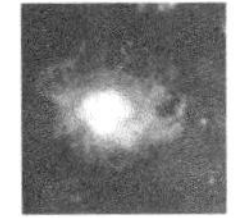

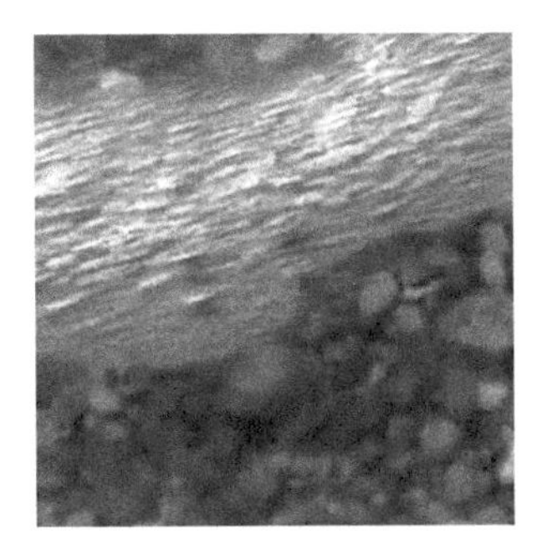

Further down is a place
Where its waters spiral
With cappuccino froth
Of summer sand
Or run cold, shrill-cry-clear,
As the kids splash in delight,
Lifting bladderwrack
With the handles of their nets

To bring forth from their hidy-holes
Green-backed crabs,
Sideways-scuttling,
All stalk-eyed
And bubbling-mouthed.
Until the bucket's full
And their shells crackle
Against one another,

To be released
At the end of the day,
When parents wrap their kids –
Too cold, to know
What to do with themselves –
In beach towels and have them
Run back to the warmth of
Teatime TV.

Once, at low tide, was there
A dogfish trapped there,
Writhing side to side,
Trying to get back
To its element. You lifted it,
Feeling its speckled skin
Sandpaper-coarse
Against your palms
And carried it to the open sea.

Once the kids found a strange
Moonage thing there as it seemed –
All legs, nearly – pale pink-grey and spiky,
Emerald weed self-thrown over its back –
A spider crab of enormous proportions!

There were the jewels of perrywinkle shells,
Which, when you lifted them on to your palm
Seemed suddenly to grow legs,
That sent the shell scurrying,
Scratchy-tickling, across it –
Homes to hermit crabs.

As it fills, you take a snorkel
And swim slowly up the pool,
Feeling the bed
Of undulating seawater
Under your belly, supporting you,
So all you have to do
Is paddle effortlessly
With your hands.
To the sides of the pool
Gullies lead away.
In these, hours before,
Drained by the receding tide,
Bladderwrack sprawled limply,
Neglected as it seemed.
But now immersed once more
That same weed stands in
Proud, tree-swaying forests.
You push your way
Between them –
Surprising a bass hunting there
Which through the lens
Of your mask appears huge,
And looks as surprised as you,
As it turns tail and hurries away.

Further on, the rock floor
Of the gully drops away
Into the deep coldness
Of open water –
The sea proper.
Here you turn and feel
Once more the warmth return,
As you approach the pool.

May 2020

Way to the Beach

Kids jump from the dunes.
'Mind that wire,' I say.
At night a fire on the beach
From fallen pine branches –
Real 'West-coast' gathering
Smokings at the Barbie –
While I, solitary as ever,
Catch dogfish on the shore.

Once the yellow Sea Cat searched
(Piloted by HRH Harry, perhaps?)
While mackerel hunted
Shoals of whitebait
Carried in by August squalls
And I caught more than
I knew what to do with,
Leaving them as gifts
For the people at the chalet.

May 2018

Storm

gathering
darkening
breaking
rolling
inundating
crashing
subsiding
retreating
calming

Deposit Non-Refundable

We took the tide from The Channel,
Killed the grass beneath the panel,
Stilled the wind with turbine blade,
Until the air no sound it made,

Took from every wave its motion,
Becalmed the waters of the ocean,
Dammed the river, dammed the brook,
From running waters current took,

Grew fields of crops for biomass,
While beneath we fracked for gas,
Sought, in energy-craved confusion
The Holy Grail of nuclear fusion,

Until all is still, Earth depleted,
Rare minerals gone, life deleted,
Blinking on a single screen
Once, hand-held image of a dream,

Our Earth, non-renewable,
Expendable, consumable.
No longer then responsible,
Deposit non-refundable.

1st Jan 2020

1250 –

Chainsaw Chainsaw

to the melody of
Elizabeth Cotten's 'Freight Train'

1300 –

Chainsaw chainsaw
Sawing so fast
Chainsaw chainsaw
This tree's the last
Saw it down
It's gone for good
Gone for firewood

1350 –

Chainsaw chainsaw
Sawing so fast
Chainsaw chainsaw
This tree's the last
Home to a bird
That sang so sweet
That never more will tweet

1400 –

1450 –

Chainsaw chainsaw
Sawing so fast
Chainsaw chainsaw
This tree's the last
The air it made
With its leaves
We never more shall breathe

1500 –

Chainsaw chainsaw
Sawing so fast
Chainsaw chainsaw
This Earth's the last
Here lived the race
Who cut it through
And sliced our home in two

1550 –

1600 –

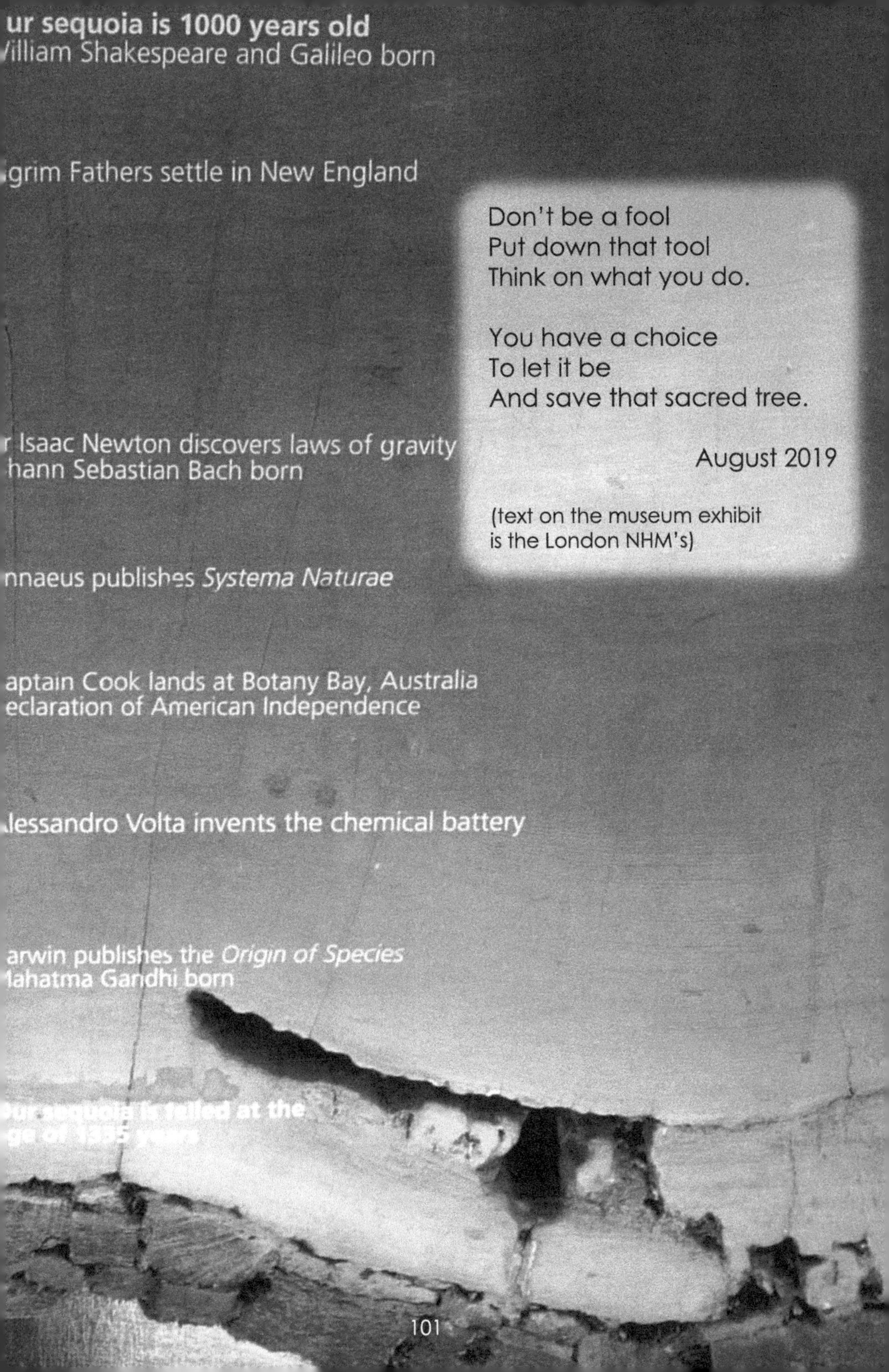

ur sequoia is 1000 years old
/illiam Shakespeare and Galileo born

.grim Fathers settle in New England

r Isaac Newton discovers laws of gravity
hann Sebastian Bach born

nnaeus publishes *Systema Naturae*

aptain Cook lands at Botany Bay, Australia
eclaration of American Independence

lessandro Volta invents the chemical battery

arwin publishes the *Origin of Species*
lahatma Gandhi born

Our sequoia is felled at the
ge of 1335 years

Don't be a fool
Put down that tool
Think on what you do.

You have a choice
To let it be
And save that sacred tree.

August 2019

(text on the museum exhibit
is the London NHM's)

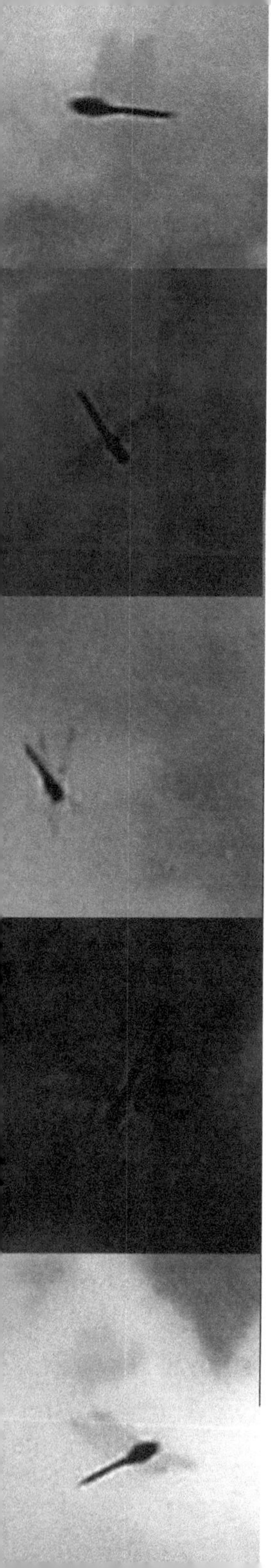

Coming Out

Skipping past the window fast,
Airborne hunter on the wing
Catches my attention.
Strong light too bright for my eyes
To take them in, other than as
Flickerings in the square
Of summer space above the lawn –
Perturbations in the air – 5 dragonflies.
What brings them here?
Ah, this: winged-ones
– Queens-to-be
From ant eggs hatched,
Now from dry earth emerge
Attended upon
Like debutantes
At some Summer Ball,
Readying iridescent wings,
To take flight,
Slow and delicate,
Up and up
To compound eyes
Quicker than my camera's
Shuttered lens
– Snicker-snack –
That registers but a blur,
Faster than our springing cat
Whose acrobatic leap
Leaves it empty-pawed.
Aeshnae with their deadly jaws
Take the queens one by one
For 20 minutes
Until all gone,
And air is empty,
Still, once more.

August 2019

Death of a Tree

You saw it upstream of the footbridge –
A pollard willow alongside
Its neighbours on the banks
Of 'small river England' –
Barely worth a second glance –
Sharing the status of the river itself
Low-lying, sluggish, muddy,
Of little account alongside
The likes of Trent and Severn –
No great tree, then.
And yet, as you reckon
(Using all the digits on one hand
To do so) how many times,
You drew, painted and collaged from it,
You see it impressed itself upon you.
Why is that? How did it?

Feel the rail of the bridge in your grip.
Smell the Himalayan Balsam
Below you in the plumb-coloured mud.
Notice the water shares the colour
Of both green and brown olives –
A perfect, perfect match.
See the trunk and branches
Reaching down to a watery sky,
Where slender leaves swim like golden fishes.
Listen to the rush of water
From the modest weir beyond,
Then draw and think and write
And IT becomes the pollard willow.
That's how it works –
The magic of the imagination.
And now here it is
(A great coincidence)
Lying fallen into the stream.
Exposed core bleached,
Spongy – lacking all integrity –
Totally done-for –
Impressing itself upon you,
For all it's worth,
One final time.

June 2020

Motley Fool

Wore a pied cloak
Gave out a croak

Flew from a crime
Stepped up on time

Dandelion crown
King for a day

Gold caught his eye
Fool flew away

June 2018

Flurry

In through the skylight it came,
In a flurry of panic
He and it colliding
In a confusion of dusty scales
And Beaujolais breath.
It dropped. He sagged.
Then up it went
Banging on the bulb
Harming but harmless
Banging on the bulb
Big and soft and dropped

And he knelt and reached down,
Tongue between lips,
So it stepped to his quivering fingertip –
Iridescent in pink and emerald–
Impossible meeting of opposites.
He carried it slow,
So there would be no disturbance
Of air against its alien fur
And, reaching the open skylight,
Lifted it on to the night.

February 2018

Foxy Lady

The level of… how shall we say… taxonomy was wrong? Choice too specific. Why not polar bear? Why not wasp – grass snake? The randomness irritated her. It was ludicrous. You want me to write something on that subject just for the sake of… Her natural impulse to destroy, to avenge, to disrupt began to boil to the surface… After a while she got up and went to the kitchen, dropped the three cups the kids had left on the side half-empty into the washing-up bowl with a 'fox', 'fox', 'fox' after each one – 'For fox sake!' she said, drying her hands (and laughing at her own joke). She picked up her car keys and left.

Just an instant was all it was – a flash of ginger dulled by mud and exhaust from passing cars was all that caught her eye. She drove to the next roundabout, circled, turned back. There was a layby near where she'd seen it. Never stopped there before – never needed to. Got out, locked the doors. Walked back along the verge.

She hadn't realized how long this stretch was – straight, fast and in her car gone in a minute. Lorries flew by, dragging cold, fume-laden air behind and landing it on her in a succession of drafts that made her shiver and glance anxiously behind. She ought to be on the other side, facing the traffic, but she might miss it. Where was it? It must have been further up – that next set of trees. And then there it was, looking very dead and dirty.

She remembered what a friend had once told her about a pheasant his dad had shot and then hung to mature and how, after a few days, he'd sworn he saw its breast heave and then again and had tapped it cautiously, so that it started to spin, sprinkling a steady stream of fresh maggots to the floor.

She poked it with the toe of her hiking boot, and felt the resistance as of some sodden fly-tipped cushion. She pushed away brambles and nettles with the backs of her legs, stamping them down, edging round until she reached the side facing away from the road. Here it was clean and fine-furred, with white teeth set along a black-gummed grin, a wavy edge of pink tongue showing – quite young, – not long dead by the looks. But for its glazed, staring eye, it might have been asleep. Foxy cunning but no road sense. Badgers, rabbits – didn't stand a chance – buzzards had a field day, and the magpies, chipping meaty pancakes off the road. A lorry sped by and from the passenger side, a man looked down on her with interest, seeing a woman in a yellow cagoul putting on a pair of rubberized gloves by a roadside, early evening.

She took a rolled up rubble sack from her pocket and shook it open, then, reaching down, took hold of the dead animal's forepaws and started to draw it, head-first, into the mouth of the sack. It wasn't stiff as she'd expected but limp, and the stink she'd anticipated when first it moved, didn't come.

With little space to move, the effort to lift it slightly so that she could ease the bag under, had her red-faced as bramble thorns plucked at her sleeves and at the bag. But now with more in than out, she lifted the sack and the fox slipped in. That was when the air came up to meet her – not quite cat, not quite dog, den-earth musk, elderberry vinegar, fish, blood and bone – old England with a little KFC on the side of a weekend – acres away from the petrol and oil of this road.

Oh, yes she thought, as she hauled it away, she wouldn't give them just a few printed thoughts. She'd give them the real thing.

April 2019

Mac is Back

It was kinda earthy – strange-earthy but it wasn't earth! What the hell was it?

She was cogitating on the inconvenience of having misplaced her driving licence and all that entails, when she saw it peering over a little hedge of parsley resting on the ice of a market stall – just the head and, judging from the size, with a good five feet of tail missing. Superior biting skills conceding nothing to good looks, it had those substantial plates of muscle on top with a slight division between, that powerful-jawed creatures such as pitbull terriers have. Its purpose there wasn't clear – certainly not decorative, that was the job of the parsley – and as horribly-fascinating as it was, would hardly have enticed a passer-by over to enquire of the price of a nice piece of Dover Sole. No, more likely, its ghastly-freakishness would have provoked a double-take as the shopper – no doubt female, horn-rimmed bespectacled, with head-scarfed permed blue-rinsed hair and ideally in her early 70s – stared back glassy-eyed, mouth agape – in kind as it were – at this monster of the deep, a good 20 thousand leagues from what any decent person would set on a fish stall let alone a dining room table. Clearly its presence there was a mistake or moribund joke. She wondered what had happened to the tail. Can one eat conger eels? Probably! Many fish species are sold as food. She'd remembered a friend – a keen coarse fisherman – who'd once told her that ever since he'd started fishing as a boy, he'd dreamed of catching a specimen roach – a handsome, silver-blue scaled fish with deep red fins. Among anglers, a roach of two pounds in weight or over is considered a specimen. In spite of decades of wet weekends traipsing about the waterways of southern England in pursuit of such a shy and elusive creature, he'd never caught one, but one afternoon had come home from work to find his wife cooking for their tea, some fish bought from an East London market. When he'd peered with interest under the grill, he'd seen there a brace of roach not an ounce under two and a quarter pounds each, sizzling away! In spite of their looks, roach make for poor eating. Not only did each mouthful resist as bland and boney the swallowing thereof, but more so, stuck in his craw as a reminder of personal failure at his hobby and a future at it where, likely as not, he would never better the sorry thing that lay discarded, half-eaten on his plate. The next day the binmen carried away the remnants of his fishing tackle. He never went fishing again.

But I hasten back to the eel head for which the fishmonger had accepted little in return, wrapping it quickly, visibly relieved by the vacant patch of ice where it had lain. As she felt the weight of it in her bag on the bus home, she knew it would be worth it. An hour later saw her placing a stool in front of her favourite chair, and then on the stool a tray with a large plate and then on the plate, the head of the eel. She turned the plate this way and that until satisfied by the orientation and then, having placed an angle-poise lamp close by, pulled down the shade until the light's beam played upon the various contours of skin and sinew over bone, bringing forth a glint from the gelatinous eye, good shadows in the nostril cavities, a nice flaring to the gill plates and so that the many formidable irregular teeth along its jaws showed to best effect. Then she shut the curtains, switched off the main light and took up her station, secured in place as it were by the board across her lap, on which lay paper and a pencil.

But the drawing would not go well. Here was a thing so alien that it seemed to resist all attempts to be reduced to mere graphite marks on paper. She shuffled about, trying to get the head 'in the round', but the arms of the chair cramped her movements. Upholstery dust drifted plankton-like across the beam as she willed herself to make the best of it. But the intensely-illuminated bubble of concentration in which she found herself almost bathysphere-like as she goggled at the eel and it gazed back, began to overwhelm her. A kind of catatonic claustrophobia came upon her. The heat of the lamp began to dull the eel's skin. She felt the drawing slipping away. With difficulty she extracted herself from the chair, went to the kitchen and brought back a bowl of water, a little of which she sprinkled over the head, before wriggling back into position.

A little of the eel's own element seemed to rejuvenate it. It began to glisten, sparkle and smile. Perhaps it had in mind a fishy joke: 'There's a party of anglers out on a boat. One of them feels seasick, and as he leans out to throw-up over the side, loses his false teeth! His mates decide to cheer him up. One of them takes out his own teeth, puts them on his hook and then lowers them over the side. He winds them up and says: "Here, Billy, look I've caught your teeth, mate!" Billy takes them off the hook, puts them in and says: "Nah– they're not mine – they don't fit," and slings them over the side of the boat!'
No doubt punctuated not by a 'boom boom' but a 'swish swish' – of his fishy tail – if someone hadn't eaten it.

Under the spotlight, the eel was clearly 'warming to its part' but so far without odorama. Then it came – the smell – kinda earthy – strange-earthy – accompanied by what felt to her like a gentle poke in her solar plexus. 'Jesus!', she said. But returned to the drawing, which was still not going well. In it, the eel looked like it was smiling – as if it had just heard a good joke. In fact, she thought as she looked at its mouth, that it could even be about to sing – yes, she'd swear it looked as if it was!
'Oh the shark has…
Pretty teeth dear…
And he shows 'em…
Pearly white…
Just a jack-knife…'
There came another poke in the solar plexus and the earthy-but-not-earth smell – 'Good grief', she said, gagging slightly, 'that really is most unusual!'

Cut a long story short, the drawing goes unfinished as she rushes out with the plate and tips the head into the black bin liner of rubbish lying on the kitchen floor. Now the smell is lodged in her nose where it remains – not even a strong one, just… very very odd. Only later does she pluck up courage to take the bag out and put it round the side of the house, with the rest of the rubbish, where it remains.

But the story doesn't quite end there, because even for a shared student house (and I speak here from personal experience) the lingering smell is bad. So pervasive is it that people leaving the house ready themselves with a deep inhalation before opening the front door and launching themselves rocket-like over the threshold, daring only to exhale when they've run the length of the garden path. The postman stops delivering. Then comes the knock at the door she's been dreading and she opens it to find standing there, two policemen. There have been complaints – it was inevitable! They ask her to confirm her name. She does. One of the policeman opens his pocket and produces her driving licence which he hands to her. She thanks them profusely, expecting any moment one of them to enquire: 'What's that smell?' But they go on their way, a good deed done.

There can be no such happy ending for the eel, though, the head consigned as it was to the deeps of some landfill for a new estate. But if ever you catch the ghost of a strange whiff coming from some methane vent thereabouts, and feel minded to put your ear to the pipe, then you might hear, but very faintly, the strains of Weill and Brecht:
'From a tugboat…
On the River…
A cement bag's…
Sinking down…
The cement is just for weight dear…
Bet you Mac is back in town.'

July 2019

Nuisance Cat Jive

Nuisance cat fried her fish
Nuisance cat cleared her dish
Nuisance cat washed her face
Nuisance cat jumped into space

Stretch
Claw
Velvet paw
Yawn
Shut eye
Before the night
And moonlight on the roof
A dream of mice
Tightrope walk along a fence
Sleeping in the afternoon

Nuisance cat smoked a fag
Nuisance cat dressed in drag
Nuisance cat sang a song
Nuisance cats don't belong

They're just a bloody nuisance.

October 2018

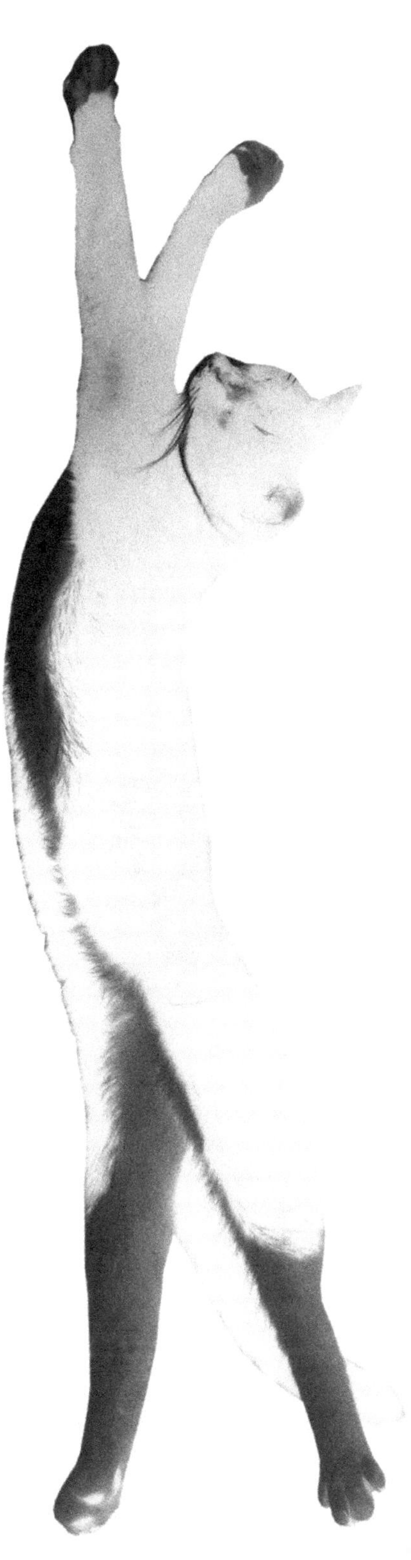

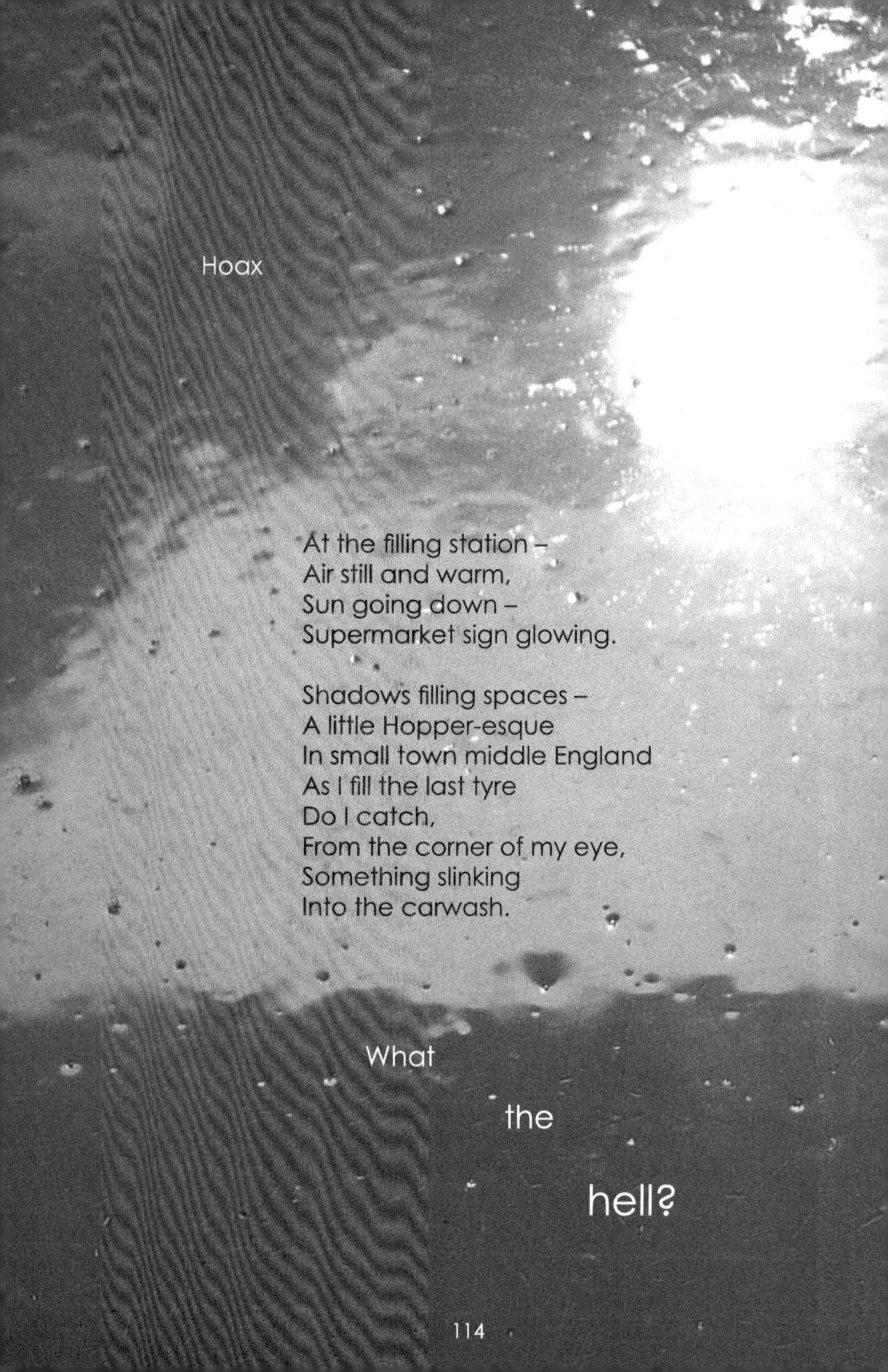

Hoax

At the filling station –
Air still and warm,
Sun going down –
Supermarket sign glowing.

Shadows filling spaces –
A little Hopper-esque
In small town middle England
As I fill the last tyre
Do I catch,
From the corner of my eye,
Something slinking
Into the carwash.

What

the

hell?

I screw on dust cap.
Straighten up. Go look.
It was big! Coyote-big!
Perhaps a fox?
Droppin' by,
For a shampoo
And blow-dry
Prior to a night,
On the town?

Walking upside the Plexiglass
Do I keep my eyes fixed
Within the space
Where mops and furred rollers
Hang damp.

Where I sense,
Sly, dry, alien fur moving through.
My eyes, gunslinger-alert,
Train upon that point
Where it will emerge.
It will emerge,
It will emerge...

But doesn't.

I imagine we are
Padding parallel,
Like opponents
In a Western movie
About to turn and shoot...

A glance at one another,
Out it comes
Silhouette...

cat

Walking cougar-slow,
Emerald-eyed,
Alongside laurels,
Muscles working,
Under faun flanks
Banded tail erect,
Too big to be a pet.

Heart-bumping I jog
To a man at a pump
And say: 'Did you see that?'
He says: 'Oh, er, yeah.'
And drives off.
He drives off.
He drives off.

The world's gone mad!

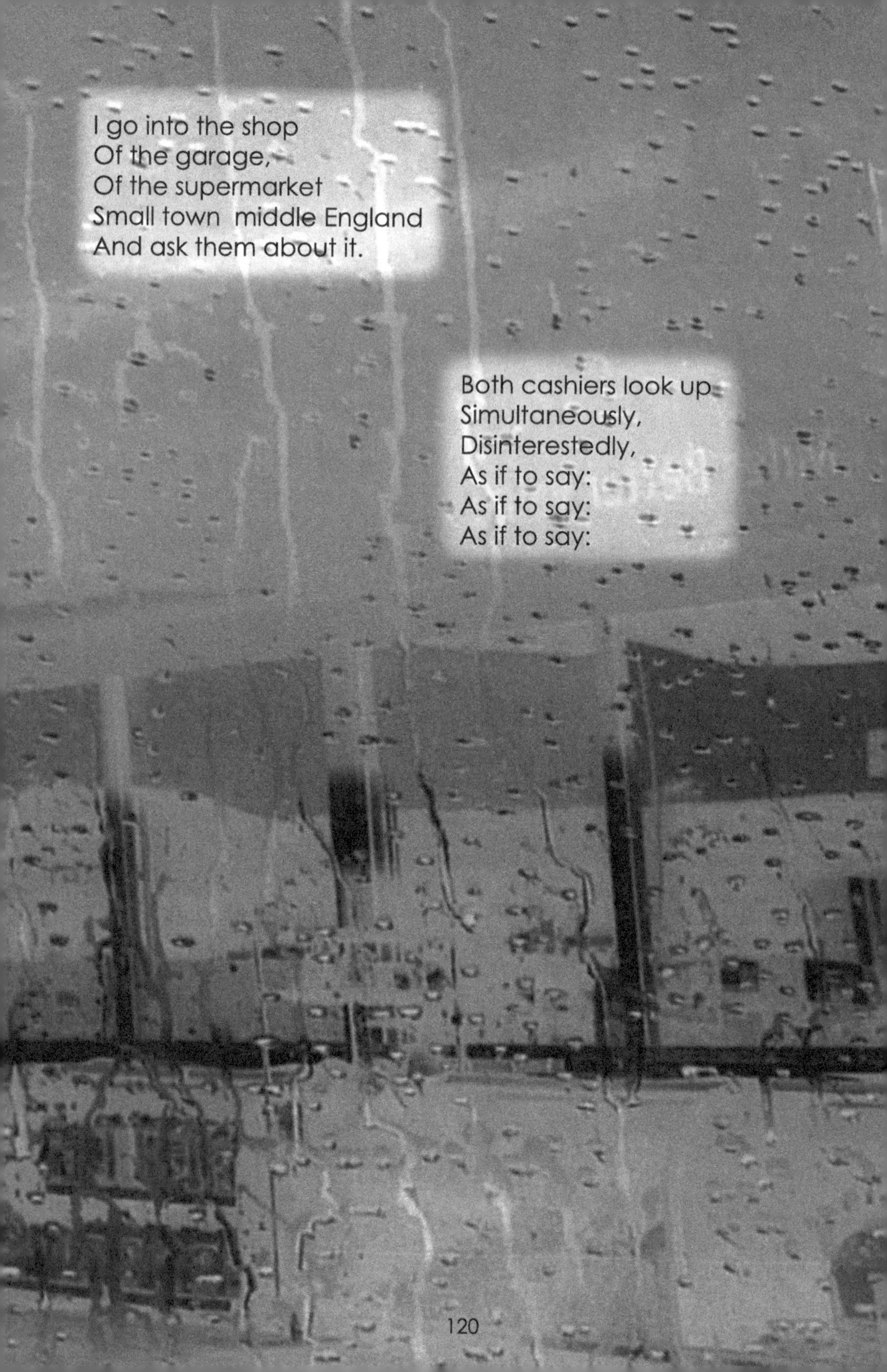
I go into the shop
Of the garage,
Of the supermarket
Small town middle England
And ask them about it.
Both cashiers look up
Simultaneously,
Disinterestedly,
As if to say:
As if to say:
As if to say:

'It's just a big-cat car-wash hoax.

It's just a big-cat car-wash hoax.

It's just a big cat, car wash...

hoax.'

October 2019

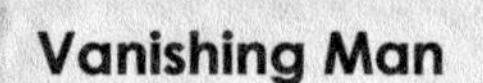

Vanishing Man

I've got eyeballs on my shoulders
Ears to my mouth
CCTV watching me
Every time I leave the house.

And the bird up there is just a drone
Perched upon my roof
That zooms right in each time I sneeze
To clock my every move.

When I was bugged, I just shrugged
No use being annoyed
When a thousand whispering voices
Could make you paranoid.

If they're looking for signs of deviance
They're gonna have to wait.
I'm far too quiet and colourless,
To be an enemy of The State.

I can pick up on their frequencies
Through a filling in my tooth,
Decipher their encryptions
Second guess their every move.

Now the only time I leave the house
Is while sleeping so it seems –
Each night beneath a streetlight
Shady meetings in my dreams.

With a man who gives me intel
That might be of use to me
But, where he gets it from
Remains a mystery.

I've found hidden messages
In the spaghetti, on my plate.
But I'm far too quiet and colourless
To be an enemy of The State.

Their algorithms rhyme
Their numbers all stack up
They've a thousand facts about you
Written in a book

Questions like lizards
Biting on their tails
With answers leading round again
As you sit and bite your nails.

Daylight behind the curtains
Channels jumping on a screen
Your life is just a programme now
On reality TV

If you're looking for answers
Through all the news that's fake
Make sure you're quiet and colourless
Quiet and colourless...

Quiet.

September 2018

Hand in Hand

I know –
You're a little worried about me.
But no need. I'll show you – I'll prove it!
See, here it is behind the bus station
The ramp – 'from-to'. Just like I said it would be.
Go down there and you can get to
Post-War Britain
To the Swinging 60s – my 'Downtown'.
To Boots to see the oil paintings
On its stairwell walls –
Rolling waves, white stallions,
Arched-winged swans –
Best Art in Britain;
To bewildering arrays of bagged toys
On Woolies' stalls 'Made in China' –
(Go on, choose one –
Don't blame me if it breaks!)
To BHS lighting Department
For a good shade
For your Nana's living room
Where there is the couch on which
You are told not to 'rile',
But on which no-one ever sits,
And under is the cardboard box
Of tinned evap. milk, fruit salad,
Good soups. Good soups, (just in case.)

To the bustling indoor market,
That smells of cheese
And where there is now,
In your duffle coat pocket,
The paper bag of Pick-n-Mix
Into which you dip your hand so often that,
On the journey home,
Sitting with the smokers on the top deck
(Best place for a view across our fields),
You'll turn green
And the driver'll stop and waits
As you throw-up
Over a Cheshire hedge.
Through the arcade
With its shops that
Like a sensitive child
Have to be kept in,
To the square and her statue
Sombre in bronze
Arcadian too –
Like some classical embodiment
Of Constance (you thought),
Holding a palm leaf
Trusted, absolute, immutable –
Always there when you needed her,
Like your mother's handbag.

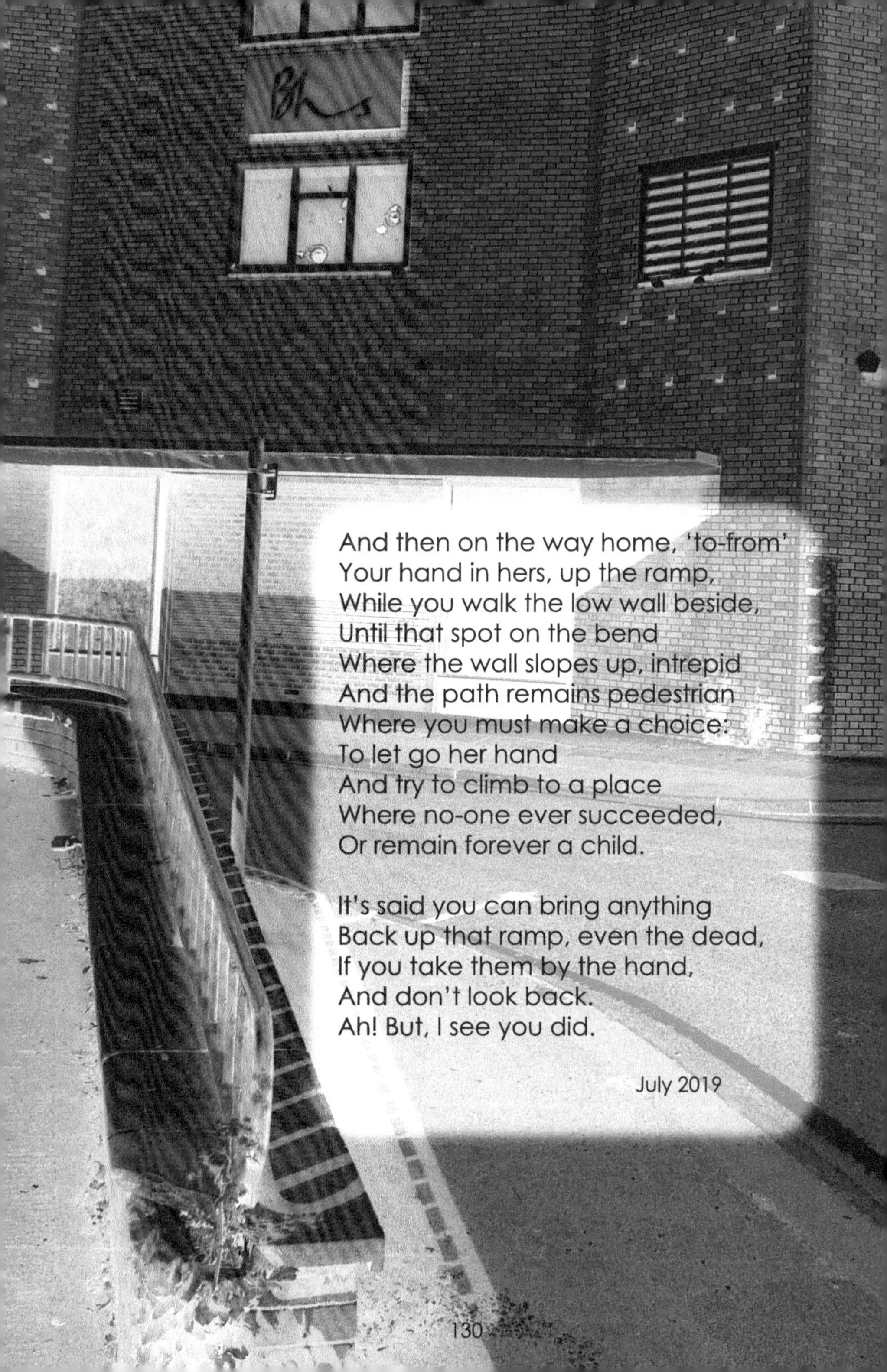

And then on the way home, 'to-from'
Your hand in hers, up the ramp,
While you walk the low wall beside,
Until that spot on the bend
Where the wall slopes up, intrepid
And the path remains pedestrian
Where you must make a choice:
To let go her hand
And try to climb to a place
Where no-one ever succeeded,
Or remain forever a child.

It's said you can bring anything
Back up that ramp, even the dead,
If you take them by the hand,
And don't look back.
Ah! But, I see you did.

July 2019

Alas Poor Bob

Up to their waists in water,
They waded with sticks, three –
One for each,
Fishing for brook rats?
Warm evening sun on their backs
When it came bobbin' steady –
Like some old, shrunken football
Greened with slime –
And the leader marshalled it aside
With his stick
And dipped in a hand
And lifted it out,
And marvelled and called
To his mates.
So they gathered round
To look into the sockets
And wonder where
It had come from
And what they should do.
Perhaps as they had with
The sand martin found dead
With a ring round its leg
Put into a shoebox
And taken to the police station,
But with no one there,
Left on the doorstep,
Another mystery to be solved?
But it is getting late
And tea-time calls.
It might have been
Crime of the Century
Or just some graveyard captive
Liberated by the brook.
Either way the leader
Let it drop.
And they watched,
As it bobbed on.

March 2018

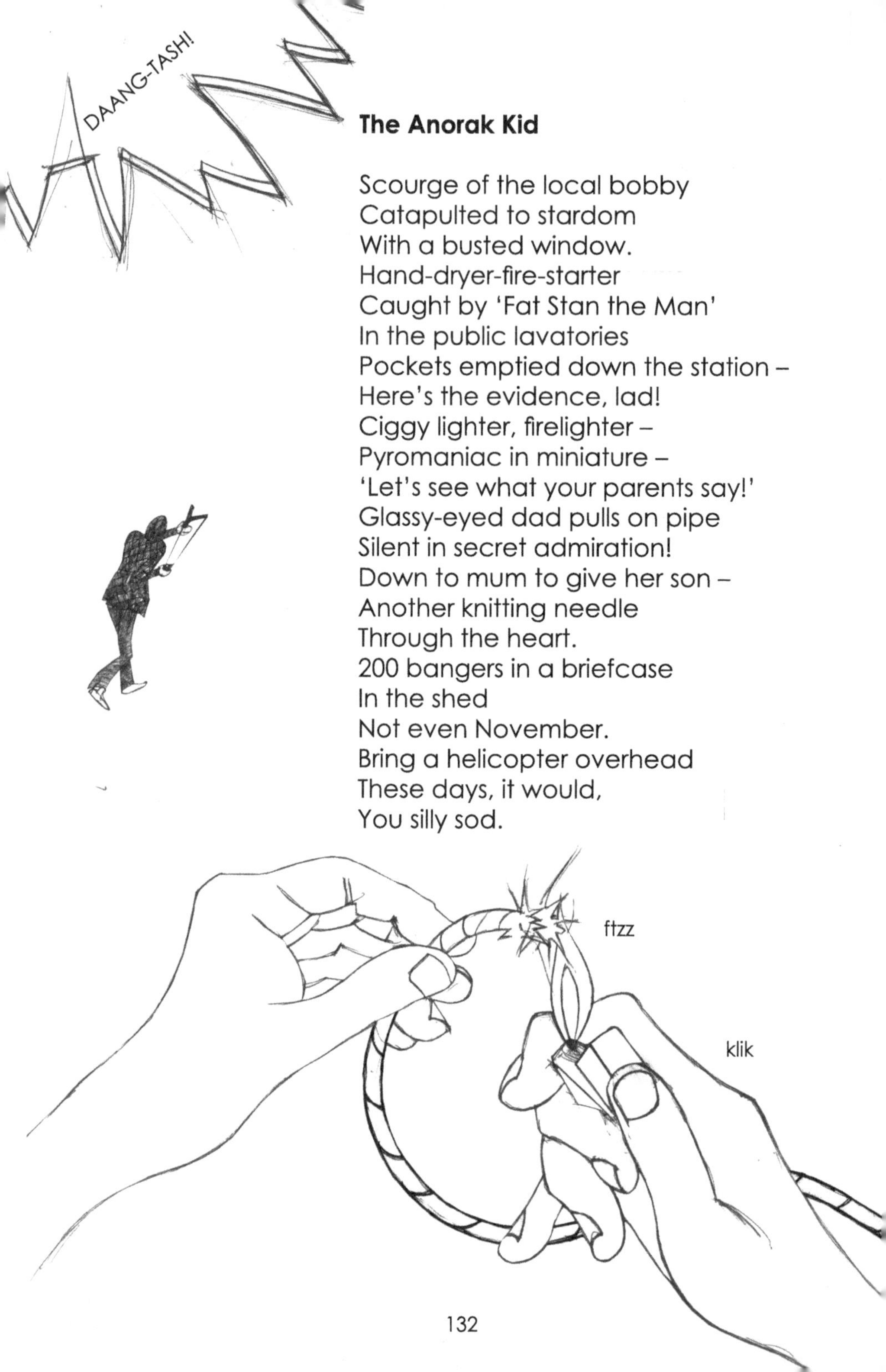

The Anorak Kid

Scourge of the local bobby
Catapulted to stardom
With a busted window.
Hand-dryer-fire-starter
Caught by 'Fat Stan the Man'
In the public lavatories
Pockets emptied down the station –
Here's the evidence, lad!
Ciggy lighter, firelighter –
Pyromaniac in miniature –
'Let's see what your parents say!'
Glassy-eyed dad pulls on pipe
Silent in secret admiration!
Down to mum to give her son –
Another knitting needle
Through the heart.
200 bangers in a briefcase
In the shed
Not even November.
Bring a helicopter overhead
These days, it would,
You silly sod.

White-haired lady
White dog walking
Looks up to a 'whump!'
And white puff in the park
From a bin across the lawn
– A Brock expertly detonated
On a slow-string-timer
That brings a mischievous grin
To the lad in the anorak.

And you led me a merry dance
With every struck-match
Dropped in the dry grass,
Letting me stamp them out
For fear 100 acres
Should go up in smoke –
You in yer bloody anorak
And the summer holidays
Only just begun!

April 2019

Play House

Showed them the magic of the imaginary –
Happy-house scribbled on a sheet:
Friendly-mouthed door,
Two bright-eyed windows,
All up on stilts, like legs,
Planned by approval,
They up on chairs beside me
At the kitchen table,
Bright-eyed and waiting to see
What would happen next.

Made that summer week
In timber from a proper yard,
Sawn in honest toil,
Hammered tight with copper nails,
Capped with pitched felt roof,
Snug and weatherproof,
Painted in a good green,
Trimmed with cream,
Windows hung with Gingham curtains,
Pale blue carpet off-cut laid,
Little ladder added
For them to scamper up and in,
And a rail to keep them safe and which,
(I thought) with sheet thrown over,
Might make a theatre,
For puppet plays with friends,
So all would point and laugh
And share each other's growing minds –
Playhouse for us all.

Year on year were cobwebs cleared,
Joints checked, re-tightened,
In readiness for still warm evenings,
When they would share a torch
And tell intrepid tales,
As they listened to the tawny owl
In the woods across the way,
Until terrified, they'd run
To the safety of their proper beds.

And year on year
Would I squeeze in
To look back up the twisting garden path
To our house and home,
And wonder at how and why
The designs we'd made,
As we sat together
At the kitchen table,
Drinking coffee,
Hadn't gone quite as planned.

October 2017

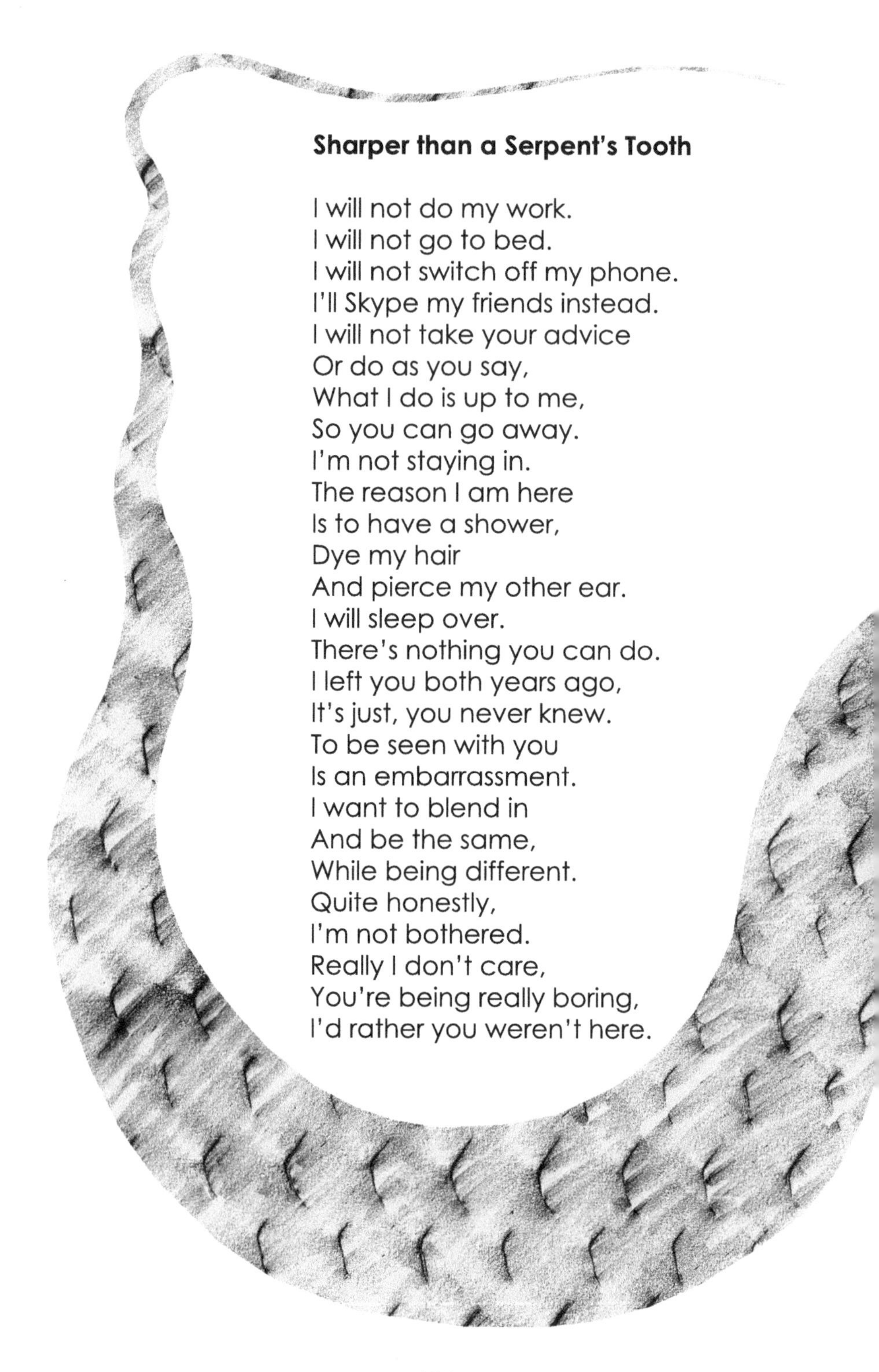

Sharper than a Serpent's Tooth

I will not do my work.
I will not go to bed.
I will not switch off my phone.
I'll Skype my friends instead.
I will not take your advice
Or do as you say,
What I do is up to me,
So you can go away.
I'm not staying in.
The reason I am here
Is to have a shower,
Dye my hair
And pierce my other ear.
I will sleep over.
There's nothing you can do.
I left you both years ago,
It's just, you never knew.
To be seen with you
Is an embarrassment.
I want to blend in
And be the same,
While being different.
Quite honestly,
I'm not bothered.
Really I don't care,
You're being really boring,
I'd rather you weren't here.

Sharper than a serpent's tooth, it's said,
Is to have a thankless child.
How much sharper for her then
Is the world outside?
If, by pushing me away,
You can find your own way through,
Then there is nothing to forgive, kid.
You must do, what you must do.

March 2017

Man in a Bottle

Looking out, he sees his family
Through the glass –
Children growing up.
He can hear them but only faintly.
His wife stands behind them,
Hand on their shoulders.
She looks at him as though
At a stranger,
And the glass is misting
And thickening.
They are growing fainter.
He looks up.
Overhead is the round,
Unstoppered opening –
The way out –
And even though the sides
Are smooth and slippery
He knows that, with an effort,
Could he, if he tried hard enough,
Get up there,
Get out and join them.
And it's because he knows
That any time he wants to, he can,
That he stays there,
Where it is still and warm,
And where the world is kept at bay.

He sees them gesturing
To him to come out to them.
And waves back and mouths:
"In a while. I'll come to you in a little while."

Some time later, he reaches up
To where the glass
Curves inwards overhead
And thinks:
'How did I ever think
I could get up there?'
Thinks: 'Now I must get out!
I must, really I must!'
He jumps.
Jumps.
No use!
There's no way up and out.

He looks out.
His family has gone.
He runs with all his might
Against the bottle wall
And feels the bottle tilt,
Feels himself falling.
The last time he fell was when he was a child,
And here he is tipping over inside a bottle
– a grown man sprawling as the bottles falls
And clatters to its side
But does not break.
He lies dazed, ribs aching.
The bottle's inner surface
Beaded now with condensation
From his exertions.
He can no longer see out.
He crawls to the neck.
He will not fit.
He entered when he was younger,
And must have stayed too long.
There is a final chance of escape,
But one involving great risk.

During his lifetime has he built
Some resource in part against this eventuality –
The slow elevating of the place where he
And his family are, above the baseline,
So that the bottle must itself be raised
Above the ground –
Quite how far, he cannot tell.
If he can roll the bottle from within
It might it be sent over the edge
To smash upon the floor,
Freeing him.

No matter that he might
Destroy himself in the act –
His fate and the bottle's
Were always one.
But what if he is not high enough,
If there is not the potential
For the bottle to break?
Why then he'll still be trapped
And further estranged from his family
On some obscure level.

If ever man made a trap for himself, this is it!
He sits with his back against
What is the bottom of the bottle,
Head in hands, ruing the day he entered.
Something must be done before it's too late!
He feels the bottle shift
And there comes a clink from the other end,
Someone is crawling in at the neck –
The head and shoulders
Of a girl in her teens appear.
She looks familiar…
And yet it can't be…
The last time he saw her,
She was barely up to her mother's waist…

"So this is where you hide yourself!" she says,
Looking round approvingly, and smiling:
"It's cosy."
"No – no, no!" he cries, in dismay.
"You can't come in!"
He pushes her out. She looks frightened.
"I'm sorry," he says,
"But you mustn't come in. You mustn't."
Her angry face disappears from the circle.
He is filled with fear and hopelessness.

After some while he moves
To the middle of the bottle
Sitting now with his back
Against its curved wall.
He pushes slightly with his feet
And leans against the curve
And feels the bottle rock.
He rocks back and forth –
A pleasant feeling.
He has control again.
'At any time,' (he thinks,
As he rocks gently),
'Can I make it roll,
At any time,
Can I send it over.'

December 2019

Rose

Mummy has a hole in her tummy,
And it's not terribly funny,
But it's not for you to know,
And it's not for her to show.

And you would have one too,
But not to pee to pooh,
If, when you nearly died,
They took your tubes outside.

So you wear it like a rose,
And hope that no-one knows.
All bagged up in shame,
A curse that bares the blame.

Mummy has a hole in her tummy.
And it's not terribly funny,
But it's not for you to know,
And it's not for her to show.

June 2019

The Waters of Babylon

'There, finally, we've made it,' he thinks. 'Success and good for all!' We were wearing bathing robes, sitting around the square pool with the pergola over, and the bougainvillea trailing, soles of our bare feet warm on the slabs, water clear aquamarine blue. Turning to his mother, he sees her face nearly hidden by the hood of the flannel robe which is up, even though it is high summer. 'She's just skin and bone,' he thinks. 'Can't get warm.' It saddens him greatly. Nothing he can do. Knows it can't be long. Her wrists are so thin. Not a pick on her. Says she eats what she feels like. But she has no appetite. Sitting between them is another as is she, but in deeper shade – not flesh and bone, just bone – and yet a simulacrum of the first. A thought comes to him. He's about to ask: 'Are you..?' And looks back to his mother and sees there now, not merely her thin frame but a bone-white skeleton. 'How long have you been like this?' he thinks. 'I never knew.' He turns to the other members of his family to his right, and begins: 'How long has she been...' and sees that they are but bone too. And he looks down upon his own hands, skeletal now and sees he's been betrayed.

December 2018

Lucky Strike – On the Scarification of Non-Gentrified Small Town Middle England by Natural Processes

Part I

The finest way to say : 'Fuck off!' to work
Is by drinking through Monday afternoon –
I get it, totally. But I remember thinking:
How can they afford it – the time, the money –
Where was I going wrong?

This was a new bar – ostentatious –
Round from the bus station (we'll come to that) –
A Wetherspoons – must have cost a bloody fortune.
As I passed by I saw the dust and filth
Accumulating thick against the base of a doorway,
Windows boarded up.
That didn't last long!

Same with the Tanning Parlour –
Two shop fronts-worth
(And the old Gaumont at the back)
With a golden pyramid in the logo, for luck.
From somewhere deep inside
Came the faint murmur
Of an alarm ringing –
Probably someone they'd left under.
(I'll bet that if you could put your ear
To the right spot, you'd hear the same
From some pharoah's tomb in Giza.)
Done to a crisp.

This town never was high-rise,
There's a kind of self-levelling quality to it,
A sort of admirable greyness,
A scaliness like reptile skin
That sheds if anything gets
Too big for its boots.
Yes, even – I suppose,
Given a century or so –
A whole goddam railway industry.

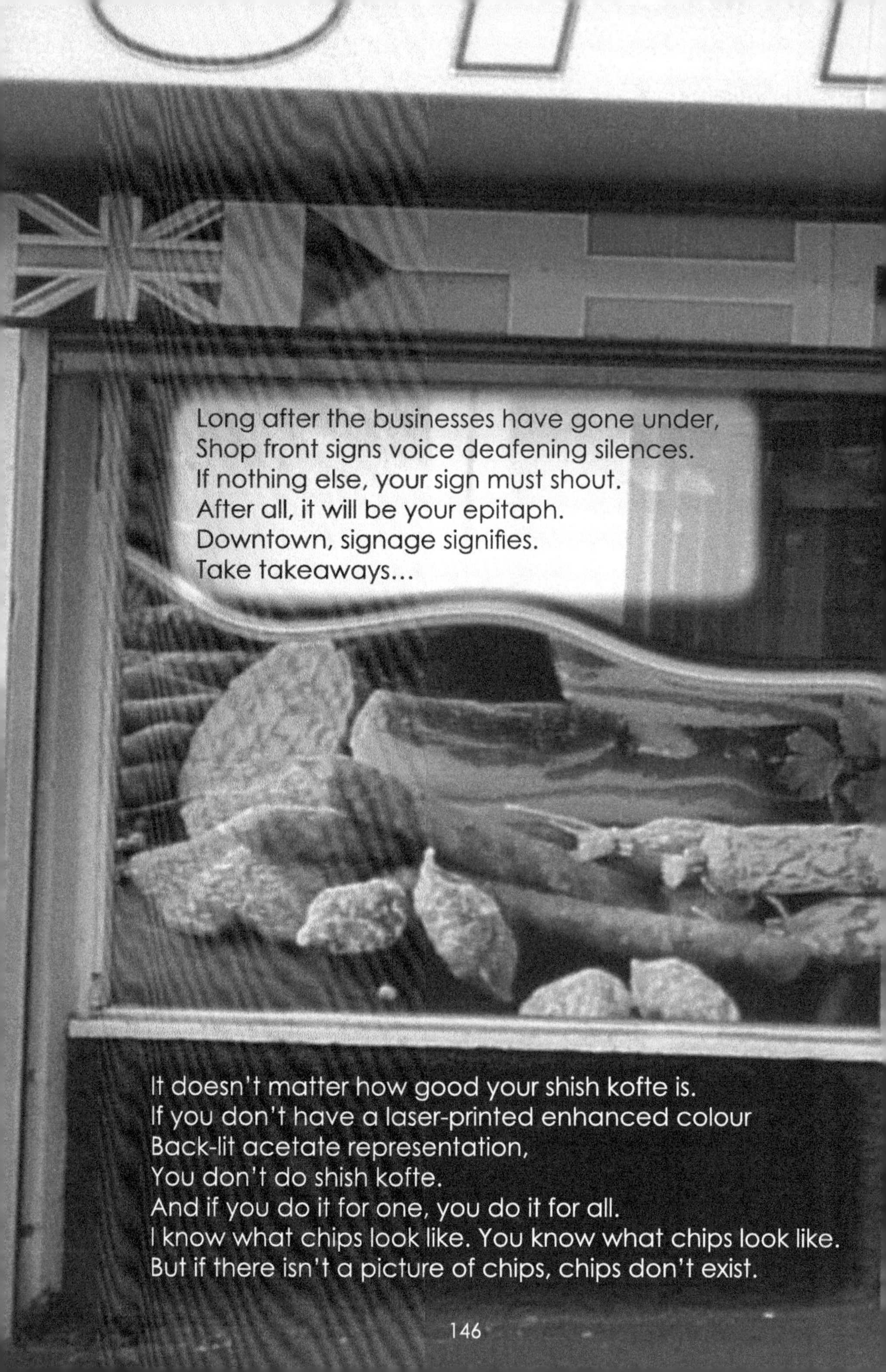

Long after the businesses have gone under,
Shop front signs voice deafening silences.
If nothing else, your sign must shout.
After all, it will be your epitaph.
Downtown, signage signifies.
Take takeaways...

It doesn't matter how good your shish kofte is.
If you don't have a laser-printed enhanced colour
Back-lit acetate representation,
You don't do shish kofte.
And if you do it for one, you do it for all.
I know what chips look like. You know what chips look like.
But if there isn't a picture of chips, chips don't exist.

On the whole,
Philosophy is for arseholes –
People like me who,
Without a second thought,
Blunder into some ill-concealed snare,
Baited with some
Low-grade tid-bit of an idea,
Only to find themselves
Catapulted feet-first
Into the tree tops of confusion,
And left to dangle
– Usually quite happily.
(Or perhaps I'm getting confused
With Queen's Park in the 70s.
Lads being lads.)

Donald Davidson had a theory of truth:
'T-statements' that matched propositions
Such as: 'Donna kebab is sold here'
With their truth conditions.
Namely that the proposition is true
If, and only if, donna kebab is sold here.
These always struck me as a bit circular.
But in Philosophy circular is good.
So that's okay.
In Ali's shop was the further component
Of the pictures. Perhaps he was
More of an early Wittgensteinian?
What d'you reckon, Ali?
He said I was probably
Over-thinking the food –
Would I like something to eat?
'Have you got an omelette?'
'Do you see a picture?'
Point taken.

Part II

As I walk, a krautrock soundtrack
From the early 70s plays –
Probably CAN's 'Paperhouse'.
Rods of icy rain dissect the winter sky
Like dry spaghetti strewn across
A cheap granite-effect worktop.
Lousy weather. Lousy writing.
An elderly couple pass in the opposite direction.
The woman turns slightly and whispers:
'Never underestimate the power of gold
In the most lack-lustre of luckless places.'
(I'd swear I'd seen her somewhere before.)

I put my hand on the St Christopher
Round my neck –
The one my mum bought for my 18th –
And as I turn into West Street
Smile wryly at the sign:
'Your scrap gold – top prices paid!'
(I take the sign as a sign.)

As I walk into the pawnbrokers
I feel eyes giving me the once-over
Starting at my shoes,
Then moving very quickly upwards
To my long, awkward-person hair,
First appearances filtering
The desperate-for-a-fix addict
Or loan-shark-victim, from the rest –
The rest, of course falling on a continuum,
From behind-with-the-rent needy,
To casual enquirer with a little spare gold on his hands
And all
The time
In the world....

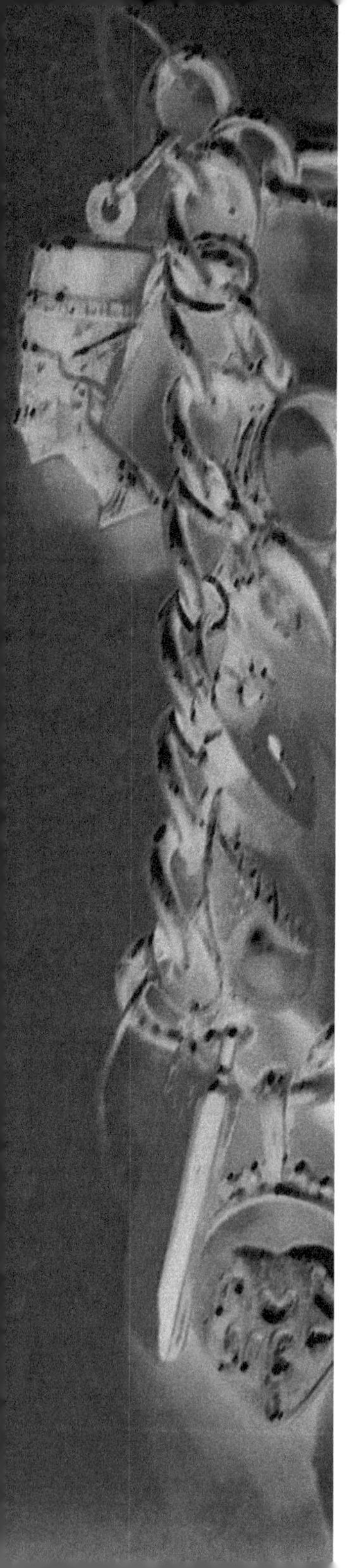

'Can we help you?'
'I was interested in selling this... chain.'
(I thought better of selling a saint.)
'Have you tried up the road?
Only we're not really taking
Jewellery at the moment.'
(I wasn't expecting that.)
'Er, well can't you just
Give me some idea – ballpark?'
'I'll have to show it to Mr Onedin.'
(Mr What? What the fuck!?
Is it some kind of shipping magnate
They've got behind there?!)
I fumble with the catch.
One of those little sprung-ring jobbies
– Should've have taken it off
Before I came in.
My nail slips.
'Nearly got it,'I lie.
I feel my ears redden.
Summoning a near Olympian effort,
Do I manage to hold open...
The tiny clasp...
Just long enough...
To slip out the slender link,
So the necklace falls... free.
Here he is: tiny St Christopher
With the boy on his shoulders,
Wading the stream.
Can't bear to think how many days' work
My mother had to do, to pay for that!
The woman offers a padded tray –
'The tray of respect' – on which I place it,
And disappears through
A little doorway at the back.
I hear her going upstairs,
Listen acutely to snatch
A word conversation
– Something – anything –
To verify the existence
Of another party – a 'Mr Onedin'.
But can't.

But I get it!
Just some kind of schizophrenic set-up,
That will allow her
To come down, sheepishly,
As the bearer (only) of bad news.
(Don't shoot the messenger!)
I look round the shop.
There's the young woman – trainee –
Standing with her arms folded.
I wonder how much a person
Could nick in one good swoop.
See the CCTV camera on me.
Right now they're (if there is a 'they')
Probably weighing up
What to offer based on
My image on a little grey screen.
(He's a praaat, offer him thaaat!)
I hear the woman returning
And affect an air of careless distraction.
She hands me the tray.
'£65's about the best we could do.'

I feel a little wave of rage pass through.
'My mother gave me that!
It's worth more than that.
I know it is!'
'We can only give scrap value
Based on weight
And the current price of metals. I'm sorry.'
I put on my voice of reason,
And say firmly and fairly:
'Okay. I'm not in a hurry. I'm not a junkie.
My mum bought me that
As a birthday present.
All I'm asking is a fair price.
Please, just have another word
With Mr Onedin.
Ask him if he can't be
A bit more accommodating.'
She sighs and, leaving the tray,
Goes back upstairs.

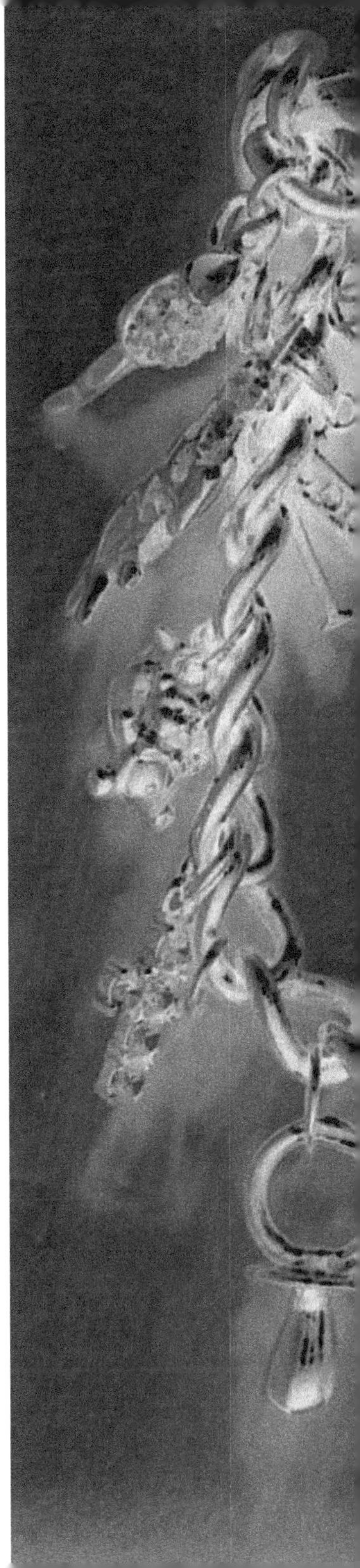

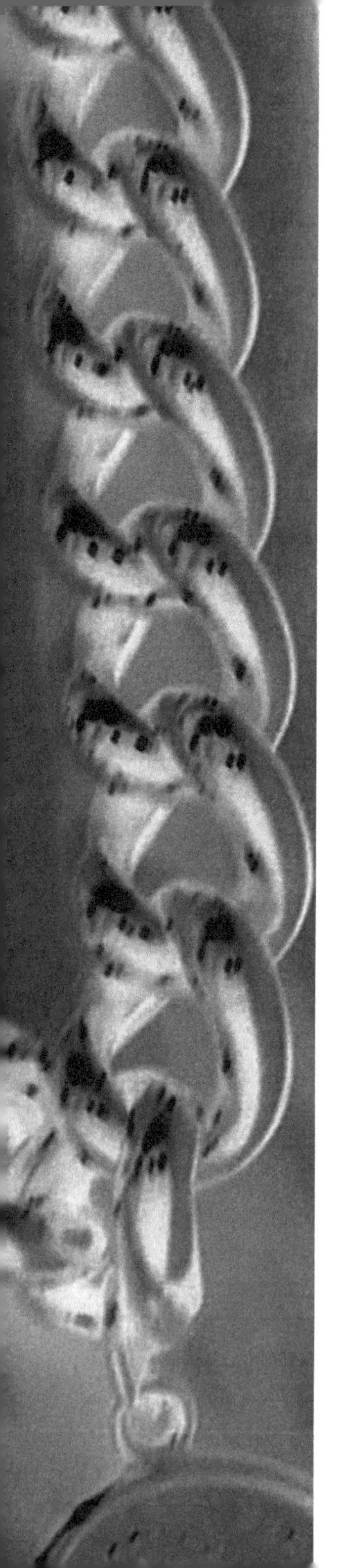

This time I think I do hear a second voice.
There comes the sound
Of two people descending.
The woman steps through, ignoring me,
And a short man as broad as he is tall,
Edges his way in –
Straight out of a story, it seems.
He's wearing a loud Hawaiian-style shirt
Of the kind you might fall for once,
If you were going on holiday to the tropics.
Has longish, well-oiled,
Salt and pepper hair,
Back-combed and held
With a tortoiseshell clasp;
Places his hands palm down
On the counter displaying
An array of fat fingers
Each encircled by at least one,
And in some cases two,
And even three, gold rings.
One hand he extends to me
While smiling expansively
To reveal a mouthful of gold-filled teeth.
'I'm sorry, my friend,' he says,
Pumping my arm, enthusiastically,
While raising his Raybans to his crown.
'It is a very nice piece, and I understand
Of great sentimental value
To you from your mother.'
(Deep brown eyes
Full of genuine sympathy.)
'To be brutally honest,
Nearly all of the items we take
Are... melted. The margins are... narrow.
I offer a fair price because
I have a reputation for... honesty.
I want people to come back to my shop.

All of these other things,
I would prefer for the owners to redeem.
That way they get their property back
– I make a little. But sadly,
Mostly this is not possible. So here they sit.
My friend, thousands of miles away
Is there a man who found a little gold.
Now he digs night and day
To keep his family in poverty.
He will never reach 40.
His children will not reach puberty.
Gold is a curse.
If people knew this, they would not buy it.
But gold is auspicious – even the colour!
You tell me what colour most of the food
In this town is and why chicken
Comes in nuggets, uh?!
It is just yellow metal
But it is not my business to complain.
Ask me my favourite movie. Go on, ask!'
'What's your favourite movie?'
'*The Treasure of the Sierra Madre*!
With Humphrey Bogart and Walter Huston!
You know the movie?'
I say: 'I do, I like it – great humour,
Acting's brilliant.'
'You do? You like it?
I like it because it is a warning to me.
Always is there a gila monster!
I'll tell you what, my friend…
Why don't we melt a bit of sunshine
And let some golden rays
Brighten up your life?
I give you 80 for your St Christopher.
My final offer! How about it?'
'Okay, I suppose.' I say, reluctantly.
He counts out 4 new Twenties from the till.
Hands them to me.
'Take it easy!
(And watch out for that gila monster!)'

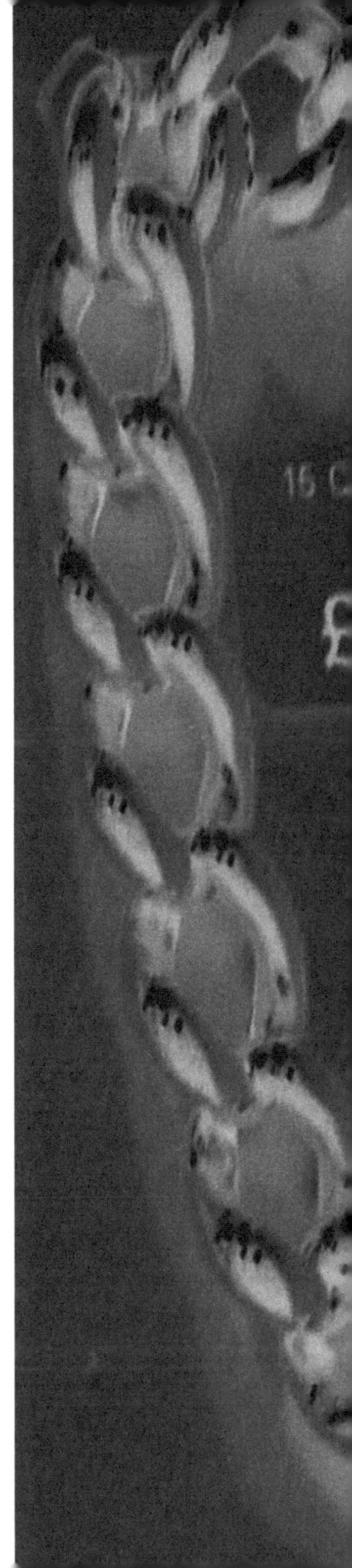

Part III

£80 is better than £65
Is better than a chain doing nothing.
I'm not superstitious! So, what now?
Parsimony! Parsimony is the order of the day.
Spend wisely or not at all.
But one has to speculate to gain.
So I'm going for an inspirational drink.
No 'cantina'.
'The Market Tavern' will have to do.
And just the one, you understand. One –
Drinking on Monday is for lushes.
But you can't deny you feel better already.
A song, a kiss, a little squeeze
All promised in a mouthful of lager top.
Never disappoints! Bonhomie.
Silly-nonsense.
You can't eke out good cheer!
Who would want to?
Same again? Why not!

One day those killjoys will ban smoking in public.
I take out the packet which has 7.
I know it has. Never looked. Never counted.
Intuition. You have to know what's important.
If there's 7 it's gonna be your lucky day.
You'll have the world at your fingertips.
But there has to be... 7. There you are.
What did I tell you? Too easy!

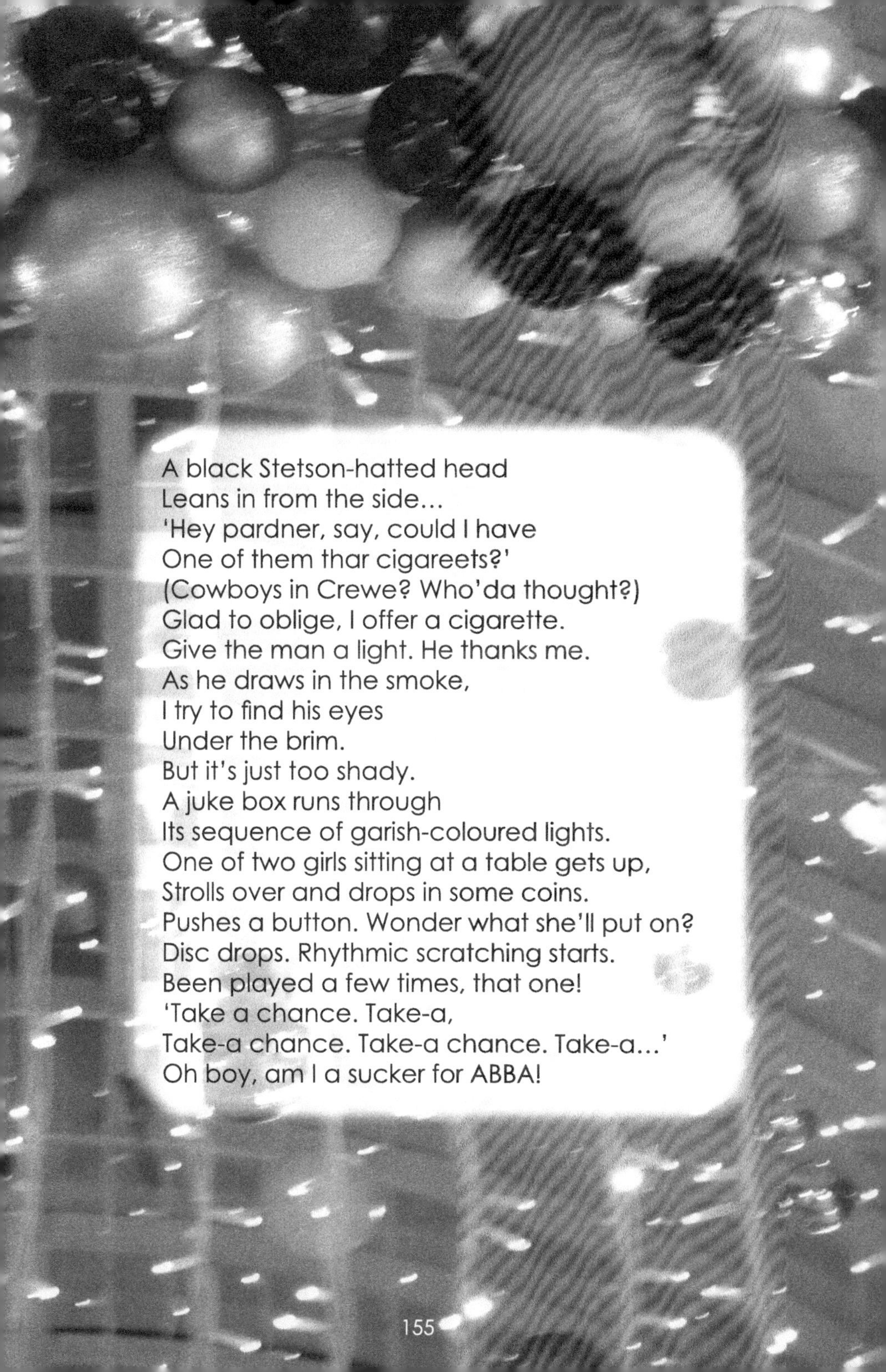

A black Stetson-hatted head
Leans in from the side…
'Hey pardner, say, could I have
One of them thar cigareets?'
(Cowboys in Crewe? Who'da thought?)
Glad to oblige, I offer a cigarette.
Give the man a light. He thanks me.
As he draws in the smoke,
I try to find his eyes
Under the brim.
But it's just too shady.
A juke box runs through
Its sequence of garish-coloured lights.
One of two girls sitting at a table gets up,
Strolls over and drops in some coins.
Pushes a button. Wonder what she'll put on?
Disc drops. Rhythmic scratching starts.
Been played a few times, that one!
'Take a chance. Take-a,
Take-a chance. Take-a chance. Take-a…'
Oh boy, am I a sucker for ABBA!

I tap my foot to the beat.
The stranger holds up
A pocket watch on a chain:
'Ever see one of these, kid?'
Opens it up – just a watch face.
'You're fast!' I say.
'Okay, so you tell me what time it is.'
'Six on the nail.'
'What year?'
'What d'you mean, what year?'
'Pick a year... And a date...'
'Er, I dunno... 1973. March 14.'
He sets the hand on a small dial
On the main face.
And presses the winder on top.
Hands shimmer, numerals move,
Face swims. Glass darkens.
It's like there's video playing,
Fuzzy but coming into focus.
A kitchen floor of red and blue stone tiles,
On it a big, wooden bucket.
'I've seen this before!'
Water slopping, apples bobbin'.
We're all in our best birthday gear.
Faces scrubbed and scrubbed again.
All spruced up, nowhere to go
But the birthday party.
Too old for this game.
But just the right age to be...
Interested as hell.

Crushes galore. Apples bobbin'.
Closest to a kiss you might share
Jane's mouth on an apple.
Susan's mouth on an apple.
Bobby's mouth on an apple.
Just a bucket full of teenage crush.
One of the lads plucks one out,
Black hair dripping over sapphire eyes,
White teeth flashing, shirt soaked,
Holds it up victoriously
Like some young hero
From Omaha Beach or Nam
And yet he might be.
Yet he might be.
Truth or dare.
Forget the chronology.
'Hell, how on earth did you..?
It's like a smart phone, right?
Can you go to any time?
Can you go to the future?'
(I look under the brim.
Still too shady.)
'You can, can't you?'

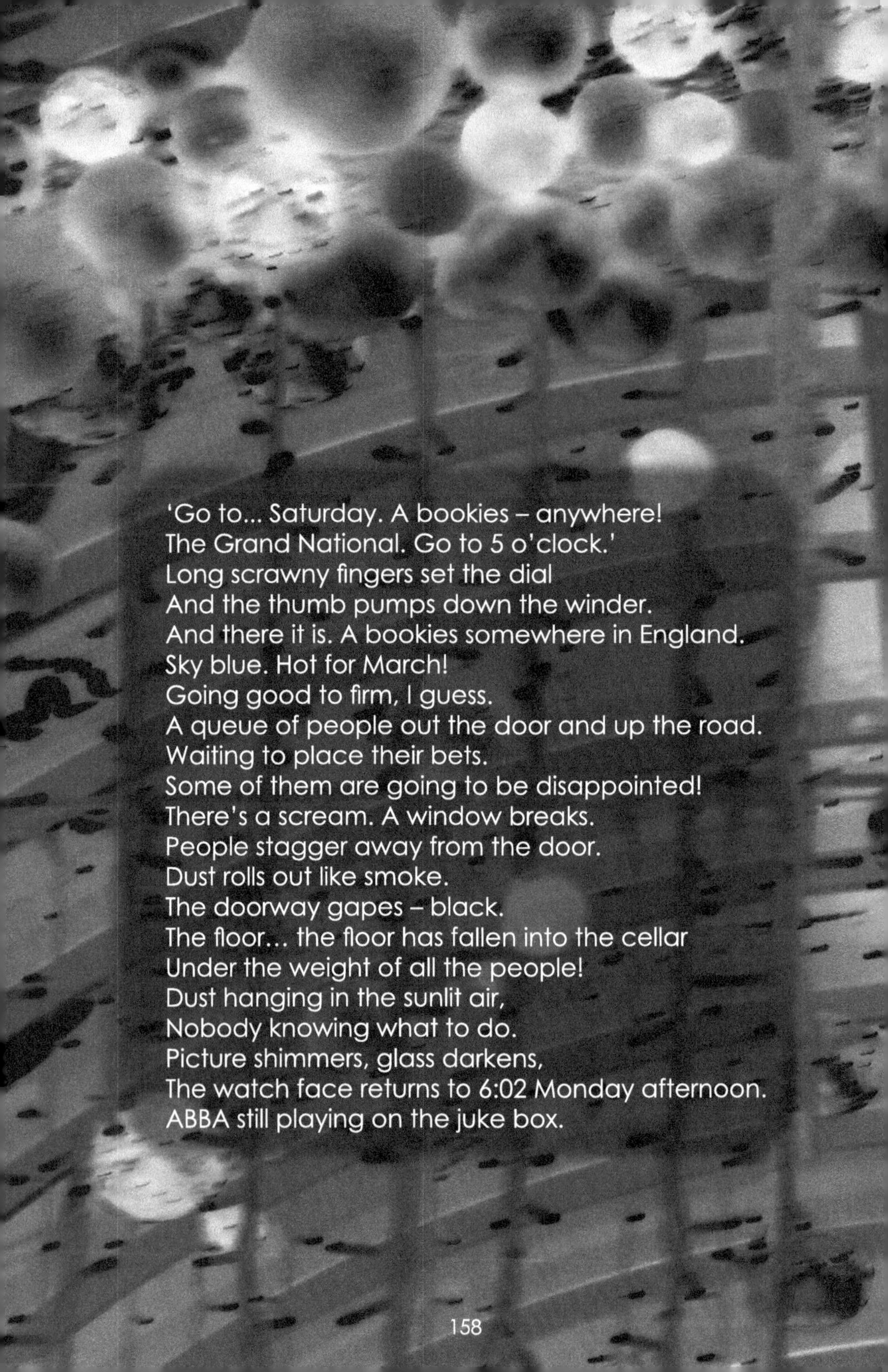

‘Go to... Saturday. A bookies – anywhere!
The Grand National. Go to 5 o’clock.’
Long scrawny fingers set the dial
And the thumb pumps down the winder.
And there it is. A bookies somewhere in England.
Sky blue. Hot for March!
Going good to firm, I guess.
A queue of people out the door and up the road.
Waiting to place their bets.
Some of them are going to be disappointed!
There’s a scream. A window breaks.
People stagger away from the door.
Dust rolls out like smoke.
The doorway gapes – black.
The floor… the floor has fallen into the cellar
Under the weight of all the people!
Dust hanging in the sunlit air,
Nobody knowing what to do.
Picture shimmers, glass darkens,
The watch face returns to 6:02 Monday afternoon.
ABBA still playing on the juke box.

'How about a little wager?' says the stranger.
'What?'
'You tell me how many cigarettes you have left.
And if you are right, I'll give you the watch.'
'And if I'm wrong? What if I'm wrong?'
'What can you put up?'
'I've got about 60 quid in cash...'
'It's worth a lot more than that. You know it is.'
'It's all I've got.'
(Anyway, I think, the point is:
I can't possibly lose –
I know how many cigarettes
There are left in that packet.)
'Well,' I say, 'what d'you suggest?'
The man leans in,
Puts a hand to my ear and whispers.
'Hah-hah! You're joking, right?' I say.
He laughs – a big, hearty laugh,
From deep deep down.
And I think I see his eyes sparkle – black.
I laugh too.
'Okay,' I say. 'Yeh. Yeh. It's a deal.
But I always know how many I've got.'
'Here,' says the stranger.
'I'll put the watch, next to the packet.
Now, tell me. How many?'
I look at the packet, and think a moment.
Don't calculate. Intuition.
You have to know what's important...
'There's just one. One left...
I need to buy some more.'
I open the packet and lift the gold foil in the corner –
The only place where one last cigarette could be.

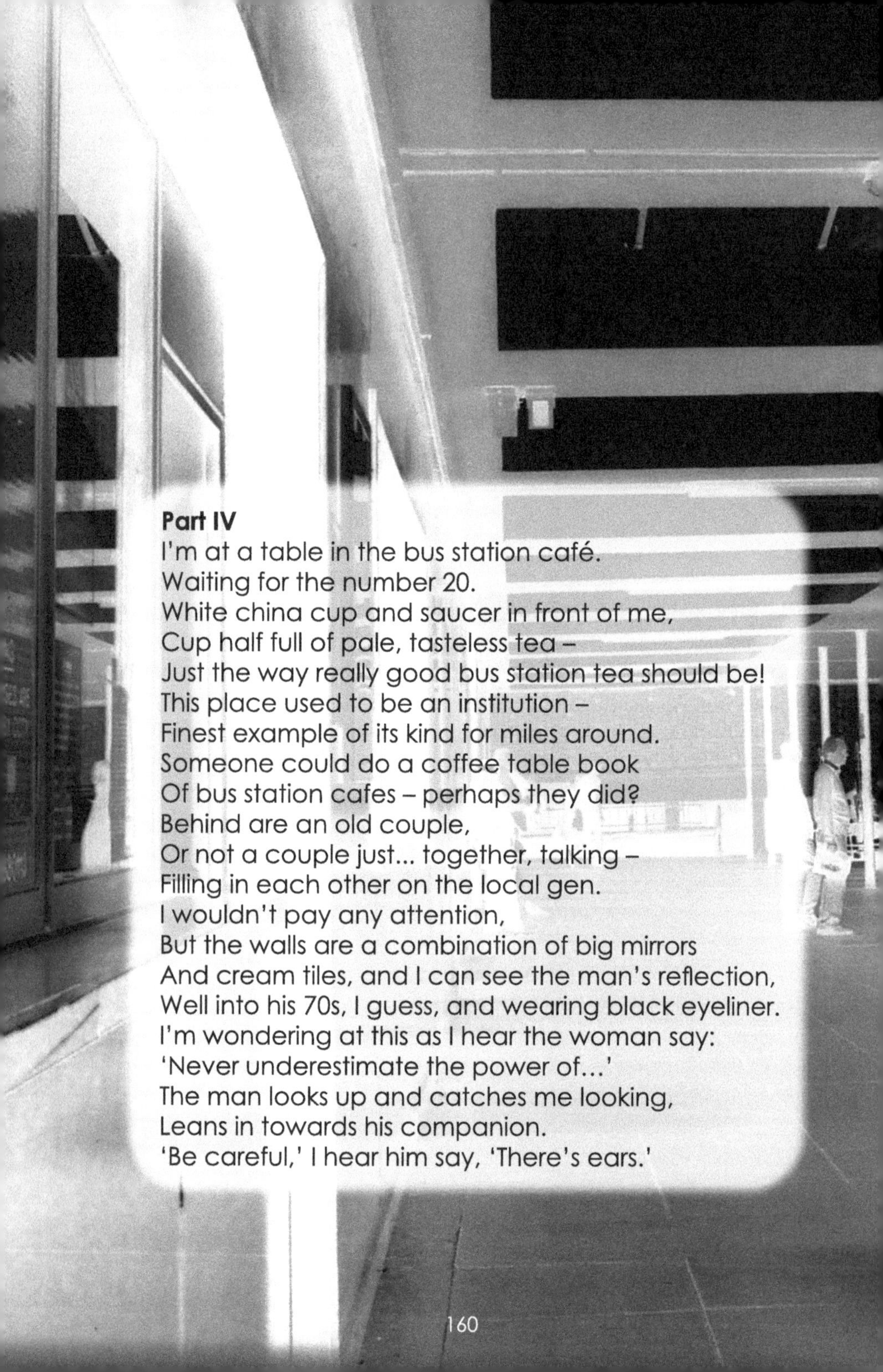

Part IV

I'm at a table in the bus station café.
Waiting for the number 20.
White china cup and saucer in front of me,
Cup half full of pale, tasteless tea –
Just the way really good bus station tea should be!
This place used to be an institution –
Finest example of its kind for miles around.
Someone could do a coffee table book
Of bus station cafes – perhaps they did?
Behind are an old couple,
Or not a couple just... together, talking –
Filling in each other on the local gen.
I wouldn't pay any attention,
But the walls are a combination of big mirrors
And cream tiles, and I can see the man's reflection,
Well into his 70s, I guess, and wearing black eyeliner.
I'm wondering at this as I hear the woman say:
'Never underestimate the power of...'
The man looks up and catches me looking,
Leans in towards his companion.
'Be careful,' I hear him say, 'There's ears.'

I amble over to the counter
And see next to the till
A basket with a label:
'Ex-juke box singles' –
Bundles held together with elastic bands.
One bundle has 'Wordy Rappinghood'
By Tom Tom Club,
Which I take to be requisite,
Except I never buy singles.
So, this'll do nicely.
In there is ABBA's 'Take a Chance' –
A bonus – probably shot to pieces
But worth a pound.
There's a pile of comics.
Which I riffle through.
Open one randomly:
'The Man in the Mask'
Wearing a black Stetson.
I turn to the back and read 'Nature Factfile':
'…venomous saliva and foul breath
With which it is said to subdue its prey,
The gila monster prefers rocky ground…'
I feel something cold at my neck,
Raise my hand and touch the little gold
Patron saint of travellers, hanging there.
I remember, I need some cigarettes.

April 2020

found poem various Ano

'Is that the bridge?'

'That's the bridge!'

'Are we going over the top?'

Right Over the Top

All aboard
For the ride of a lifetime.
The last you'll ever take.
(You'll never want another.)

All steel and sky
Like a fairground gone wrong
(I heard someone
'Evel Knieveled it' once
In a Volkswagen Beetle.)

'Is it safe?'

'Is life safe, kid?'

Just metal and air!
Coast & Roll
Fly high
Scrape the sky
How safe can that be?

Fasten your seatbelts
What doesn't kill you...

You'll laugh 'til you cry!

Hold on to your hats
Here we go
What goes up...

All aboard!
Have a nice trip... →

May 2020

County Lines

Hoods up, subway boys on bikes
Scoot down underpass
Between estates.
Every rat a run,
Every run a rat,
Rat a tat at a door, a score,
Delivery for someone.
Lying on a duvet
Wrapped in wraps
Poorly ill taking pills
White and pimpled
Pupils dilated,
Just a cold,
Had it 18 months,
Shivering, but can't shake it.

There are farms here,
People disappear here.
Comms, crimes and scams
Run along county lines
While the yellowing grass
Sways in salty air.

9mm – not much tolerance
For someone of his calibre,
Bolt shot back on a container,
On an industrial estate.
Just a call is all it takes,
The order to: 'Contain it!'

Hoods up, subway boys on bikes
Do the rounds,
Hare and hounds,
Dependable,
Like paperboys of yore,
Pedals flying,
Messages delivered,
Scores to be settled,
Along county lines.

The County Set,
Paralytic on a town bench,
Struck dumb against a wall,
With a little community spirit
Left in a bottle in a shop front doorway.

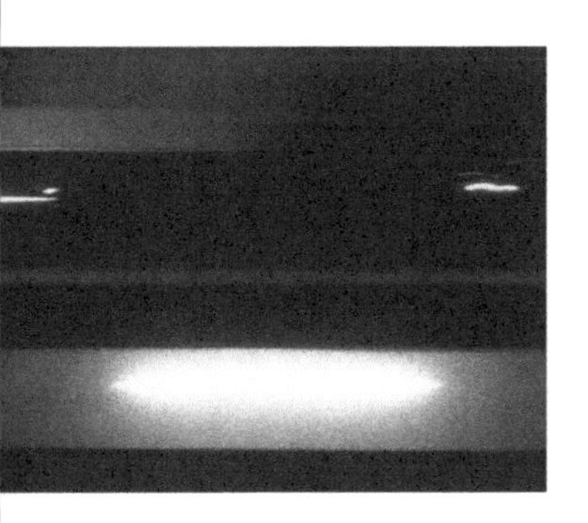

There are farms here,
People disappear here.
False IDs
Dodgy doormen
A little unhinged
Like a bull at a gate
Money talked
Passes checked
Packets passed
Turns a blind eye
Lost in a fight
With a rival
Over nothing,
Gated, suited and booted
New England
Run along county lines.
Run along, son.
But keep your nose clean.

April 2019

Verdict

The irony is not lost…
Here is Kafka's castle and trial rolled into one
Great edifice like the Mill of Justice,
Wheels of Law grinding exceedingly slow but fine.
Small doorway arched and set into rock,
Through which we pass
Not like Josef K's for him alone,
Or me alone, but for a line of us,
Waiting apprehensively, while those in front,
Pockets' contents emptied into tray,
Raise their arms in submission
To G4S bodyscan.

Court staff bump by, grumbling as they carry in,
Through the same door,
Chairs, wrapped in plastic.
'We shouldn't have to do this!'
It seems unjust and anomalous,
Court admin, deliveries, removals,
All rolled into one.
(Very Kafka.)

Security forgets to tell me which way to go so,
Unsure of my path, I return to ask,
But now, he's on the person behind.
I wait politely. The worryings begin –
Like at A&E as you sit with a loved one
And see a patient's form dropped to the floor
Go unnoticed, or a dangling tube –
Detached, possibly?
Not merely signifiers of failure
In this instance, you think,
But failure systemic –
Of a broken nation –
No cures, no justice,
Risk and danger all around.
Hah! Kafka-esque paranoia!
Get in and follow the herd, you idiot!

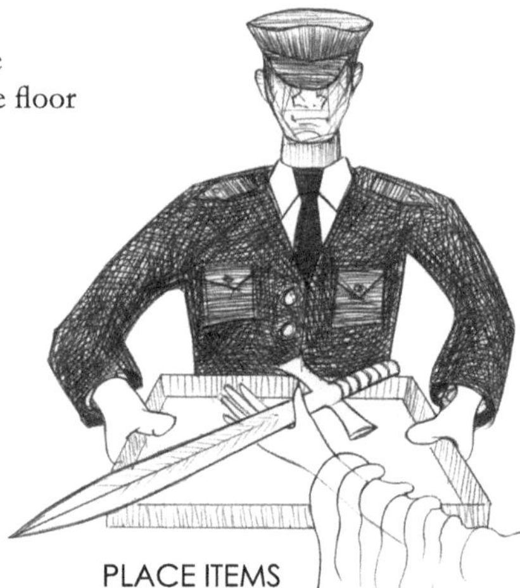

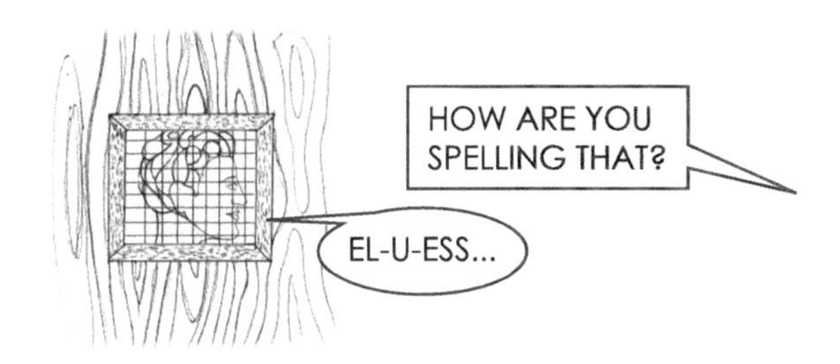

Peering occasionally through the little wired-glass window
To where the first batch of 4 are being ID-checked
And signed-in, we wait self-conciously,
Aware of an order, not wishing to jump the queue –
Mindful we have a collective responsibility
To sort ourselves out and act, in all fairness,
– as a jury.

At each doorway passed, more formalities fall away
Until the Rest Room –
Adequate – just – but too hot,
Where people talk and read and lounge
And take water from a dispenser –
'Old hands' mostly.
But for us, green to the ways,
We're ill at ease and,
With social niceties still to be observed,
Remain largely silent except that,
As on some first day at school, or work,
Or in the Armed Forces,
Is there the Courageous One who,
Unfazed by it all, smiles and jokes
And shares a conspiratorial word or two,
As though he knows everyone,
And what must be done.

A drinks machine, out of which
No-one can get what they want,
And that spits rejected coins to the floor,
Proves an ice-breaker as a bearded, wild-haired gent,
Who looks as though he might
Have wandered in from a daycare centre,
Declares it to be: 'a law unto itself.'

Showtime!
In she bustles, big hair, smiling, short, shrill
Holding up the sheet of paper
Calling for attention –
Enjoying herself!
Apologises for the lack of chairs,
Lack of air in this heat.
'All the windows are down as far as they'll go!'
(They are.)
More people enter. Standing room only.
Promises a video when she gets back.
For the first time, uses the 'C' word:
'Jurors for Courts 1 and 2 follow me,
You can wait in the library!'
Perhaps that's where those chairs were headed?
(You do that don't you – when you're nervous –
Try to make sense – grasp at straws, look for clues.)

Returning, she deals with essentials –
Sandwiches and drinks from M&S,
If we want any, but not until lunchtime.
(Bring a packed lunch in future, she chides.)
And then the video...
Definitely not '12 Angry Men';
Or the courtroom scene from 'To Kill a Mockingbird';
More like a preflight safety video –
Soulless CGI introduces key players, procedure
And our duties clearly and simply,
– Just enough for folk like us to take in.
Warming to her task,
Prepares us for the unpleasant,
Drugs, knives or stained clothing –
Evidence that we might have to look at
But that we will not be allowed to touch.
No fictional narrative.
Kafka gone.
And now: 'Is there anyone here we recognize
Or know or have met before?'
Slowly, the Courageous One raises a steady hand
On an arm a little crooked at the elbow,
In the style of the 'bad lad' in class,
And she asks him to explain…
Which he does – some connection with a person
At his table – but not one for concern.

Have we any questions?
On a roll, the Courageous One asks about
Reimbursement for loss of earnings,
How to claim expenses.
Says she'll go through that with us in a minute
Because (sarcastically) she knows how
'We will all of us have read
So very carefully through the notes
We were given before coming to court!'

Cites rules and regulations
Seemingly as complex and stringent as English Law itself,
Evidence of fares and fees paid,
Receipts and tickets kept
That must be submitted,
Otherwise, we haven't a leg to stand on.
Draws our attention to the fine
That might be handed down for submitting a false claim.
'The team are up to every ruse –
Don't try anything!'
Then a summing up:
We can expect lots of waiting around. (Bring a book.)
Punctuality: '10' means: 'Not arriving by...,
But here and ready to go into court by...!'
Reminds us that during trial,
We must not speak about the case outside
Or communicate anything about it on social media.
Says that in all her years of doing the job,
She's never experienced
Any nobbling (jury tampering)
So we ought not to worry,
But that outside, we shouldn't approach
Anyone we recognize in court,
And that if we are approached about the case,
We must make it known to the police.

Goes pally again: it's unlikely we'll be needed just yet,
As a couple of trials have only just got under way.
Smiles wryly: it's usually later on,
As the plea-bargaining system kicks in,
That defendants suddenly
Get their memories back!
Suggests now would be a good time to stretch our legs.
The Courageous One picks up a Zippo and a packet of fags
And heads out with a couple of other men from his table,
They look pleased with themselves.
Allegiances are forming.

Our first encounter with a real authority figure
Comes after lunch as the Court Usher –
A tall, dark-haired woman in a gown,
That reminds me somehow of an Indian Runner duck –
Enters briskly and assembles jurors
For courts 1 and 2. Checks off their names –
One's missing. 'She's in the toilet,' someone offers.
They wait, and out comes the woman, a little red-faced.
All present, the Usher holds open the door
And they trail away.
By 3 we're free to go, but must return
For 10 am. Prompt!

Next morning, nothing much happens.
We wait. (She was right about that.)
And I read. And watch. And listen. And read –
'A Hero for High Times' –
(100 pages romped through already –
Wouldn't be able to do that on a normal day!)
People talk easily about their journeys in,
Preferred modes of transport, jobs.
Some from another court have joined the pool,
Waiting to see if they will be called again
Or signed off – their service complete.
You might do several cases over 10 days,
Or none. The idea is that it is random.
A body of people put together at the last minute,
Gives the best chance of a fair trial.
16 people's numbers on the backs
Of playing cards, shuffled,
12 pulled out to form a jury.

There are faces I saw the day before.
The Wild One in trackie bottoms, sandals
And a T-shirt not quite up to containing his belly
Talks intelligently about how it's his second time.
I wonder, rather meanly, if it isn't a service
That bestows instantly a sense of importance
And self-worth that might otherwise
Be lacking in people's daily lives?
There's a small, middle-aged man
Wearing a suit and tie of the kind you see
At weddings and funerals –
Over-dressed, he looks out of place.
One is apt to wonder if someone
With such unreliable dress sense
Could make a reliable juror.
Pure prejudice! It's how we function.
Most of us are dressed smart-casual
– hair combed, men clean-shaven.
Probably out of a sense of respect for…
For… what...? Whom...?

Before lunch, jurors arrive back from the courts.
One can't help but try read in their expressions
What their case might be… 'about'.
But there is no uniform collective demeanour
That says: 'murder' or 'rape' or…
A lad with dyed blonde hair who looks to be in his teens
Sits down with two women and clowns around,
Joking and laughing – making them laugh too.

In the afternoon The Lady with Big Hair returns
Readying us with the news that:
'They need a jury for Court 3.'
Bags are stowed in lockers,
Last minute visits made to the toilets.
The Court Usher comes in with a sheet of paper
With the names of the people that are to go with her.
If our names are called, we must indicate that we're present.

There is a spot somewhere just below the nape of the neck
Where sharp words go in and make you jump slightly
Not quite like being shot but certainly shocked as,
After the fourth name is called
Mine is read out, and I hear from somewhere,
The croaked reply: 'Here!'

The Usher tends us in the way
Of a mother goose leading her brood –
Ever alert to the intrepid wanderer heading off,
Or the straggler who has yet to join us.
Gathers us in a corridor. Counts heads – twice.
Now we enter the building proper –
All oak and wall hangings.
If Law had a smell, this would be it –
Floor polish, good wood, fusty velvet – tradition.
Now, both a sign on the door of Court 1, and the Usher,
Warn us to be silent. She leads us by
Wooden screens with gothic carvings
Which we pass in reverent hush,
And hear there low, echoed, intonings
– of some court official, perhaps?
Then up an ancient oak staircase
With steps that creak to the tread we go,
To a waiting room where, it is explained that,
In a few minutes, we will be lead into Court 3
To sit on benches there, while we listen to the charges
Brought against the Defendant.

After, a jury will be selected,
and those whose numbers are called
Must take their places on the jurors' bench,
To be sworn in.

Those not selected will remain seated
Until being lead out of court.
And so now, maintaining a respectful distance
Between ourselves and the person in front,
And watching our step,
Do we file in, no doubt looked upon
As we sit to find everything and everyone in place –
Like a set for a TV drama – waiting silently just for us.
Up there to our right is the wigged judge,
To the front, the court officials,
And counsels for the Prosecution and Defence,
Over there the family, possibly of the Defendant,
And there in the dock, the Accused –
Only one component is missing – a jury.

Back in the Rest Room a little while later,
I wonder if there was a reason I was not chosen,
And whether the others feel, as I do,
Rejected and little disappointed
But at the same time, relieved –
After all, a case like that… or should I say:
That case?
That case I would have found hard to endure –
Unbearable, even.
Perhaps they could see that as I flinched,
As each of the 19 counts was read, in detail,
– Knew I wouldn't be up to it.

At the end of the afternoon,
Jurors from Court 3 return
And again we try to read faces,
But this time with sympathy, because we might imagine,
What they have had to sit through.
Gradually, in all this I begin to see the cost,
The first among many, this one to personal innocence,
To know now, that such things might, and surely do, happen.

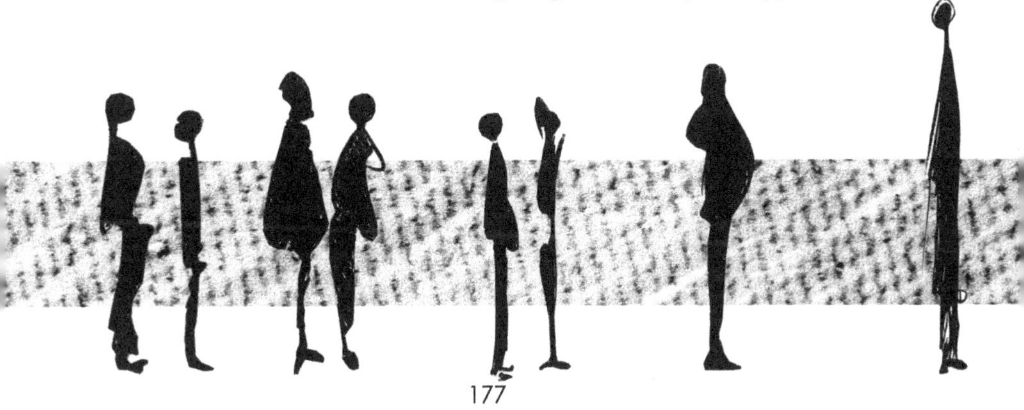

There are laws about what a juror can and cannot tell.
When a trial has finished, I can tell you
About the case. But I cannot tell anyone,
Without breaking the law,
About what takes place in the Deliberating Room.
So now, to see a way through to tell you…
What?

The ending is easy enough –
The delivery of a verdict by the Courageous One
Who takes on the further responsibility
Of being our Foreperson –
Spokesperson for the jury –
(Yes, he was one of the 4 not chosen.)
But where to begin?
Perhaps here in Court 2 after lunch on the third day,
As we stand and I await my turn to swear on the Holy Bible.

Even with 7 having gone before me,
To read those lines will be ordeal enough.
When my turn comes I start but am interrupted –
Immediately – from across the court, by the judge – the judge!
Telling me – me – one of no consequence,
Who might (as I would have hoped) have remained
All but invisible throughout this trial
To everyone in this large courtroom,
Were it not for the fact that I have failed to see,
Against the white paper on which
The oath is written, the white
Antibacterial covering of the bible
That was handed to me and
On which I must place my hand but have not,
So that I am swearing on thin air –
That I must: 'Please, take the book, sir!'
I wonder whether it will be read as it is,
As a nervous oversight or,
As a sign of open rebellion,
Or an evasion by one of little faith,
Or of an inobservant juror, not quite up to it.
So now I say:
I 'will give a true verdict according to the evidence'.

The Defendant stands before us,
In the witness box, wide-eyed with fear.
Make no mistake fear it is,
For if we feel this on our side,
How much more so must he on his,
Carrying, as he does, the extra burden
Of the accusations against him?
Remember: he is innocent.
He must be, for according to our law
He is innocent until proven guilty.
But the formality of a Crown Court
Is not impartial. It's procedures run
With machine-like determinism
And yet remain mysterious and arcane,
Down to the wearing of wigs and gowns
Which must be done, even though,
In this heat, it is clearly impractical.
So that even to the innocent,
The very fabric of the court itself
Is an intimidating reminder,
That if one is minded to break the law,
One should think twice!
You can hear the dryness in his mouth
As he confirms his name and address,
Coughs drily and is asked by the judge
To 'please speak up',
Is asked if he would like a drink of water.
He would.

Standing before his laptop
Counsel opens the case for Prosecution
How 'We will hear that…' and so on, and so on.
It seems there's no doubt a crime was committed.
I guess that's already been established?
A short break before the first witness
For the Prosecution appears.

So now we enter the Jury Room.
Here is a place sealed hermetically from outside influence.
Mobile phones have been taken away.
There can be no real-time guidance to procedure
Even from the Court Usher who leads us in
And leaves, closing the door upon us
To wait outside.

This is where a jury must sort itself out.
As yet, there is nothing to be deliberated upon,
No evidence has been given or witnesses heard.
One might imagine that people talk
About what they've seen and heard so far.
How will we know when we're to start talking about the trial?
Who makes the rules in this room?

Back in court, we listen to the case for the Prosecution.
There is a story to be got straight.
Names and complex family relationships noted.
They've given us pen and paper.
As I am minded to write, other jurors do so too,
Prompted by unanswered questions, no doubt –
Loose ends, gaps to be filled.
I think: if I can fill the spaces,
The story might be got straight.
If I can get all the facts.
Then I can get clear in my mind what happened.
Then I can decide –
Make my contribution to the jury.
What did happen?
A witness is called.
Says she saw the Defendant:
'As clearly as I am standing looking at you here now.'
But the Defendant has said he was elsewhere.
Is the witness mistaken?
Is the Defendant not telling the truth?
Her word against his.
Prosecution versus Defence.

Piece by piece,
The story builds in complexity.
One sees a picture emerging
But it will and should –
If the prosecutor is doing his job!
He wants us to find the defendant guilty.
Argues his case to that conclusion.
But what did actually happen?

We are shown evidence of damage
To a doorway photographed by the police.
Poor quality snaps,
Lacking context, but providing another piece
In Prosecution's picture.
More and more to bear in mind.
And yet the pieces never seem to connect,
Never quite to give the entire picture.
What did happen?

I can't tell you what happened in the Jury Room
Without risk of imprisonment.
But one might imagine jurors try to solve the case,
Use reasonings and even personal knowledge
Of such-and-such, perhaps to challenge
A witness's account of what has happened,
Or to endorse it.
But one might also imagine that it might be said
The detective work has already been done,
The evidence gathered
(As much of it as can be)
By the police – that being a part of their work –
And that it is not a juror's job
To play the detective.
So what is the job of the jury? When does it start?

Back in court, a policeman gives evidence,
After which a witness for the Prosecution
That should have shown, does not.
There follows cross-examinations by Defence,
Questioning the witness's ability
To identify the defendant,
Attempting to putting some of the police procedure
In a dubious light.
Case for the Prosecution concludes.

Next morning, Defence puts its case –
Not so much a different story,
But one that throws doubt on certain key points
In the case for the Prosecution –
One that implies the truth lies elsewhere.
We are taken to watch CCTV footage.
Gradually, it dawns on me
This story never can be got entirely straight.
It's not even as though we are watching parts
Of a factual TV programme with bits missing,
Or reading an impartial report with sentences redacted.
Here are two sides of a story
That must come via these parties,
Each with opposing interests,
So the presentation is adversarial,
Necessarily then with contradictions.
But can't these be sorted?
If they can, not by us.
Again, that job's been done –
By the lawyers, as best they can,
With their legal arguments.
So we are not detectives,
Neither are we lawyers.
What is the job of the jury?

Well, we have to decide on whether the defendant
Is guilty or not guilty of the charges faced,
Based on the evidence given in court and,
On the judge's guidance.
And you might remember the oath:
'A true verdict according to the evidence'.
The evidence is all that matters, surely?
And yet…

If the law really did proceed
With machine-like determinism,
It might be all the fairer,
For everything would be done by the book
And if the book was good
Justice would be so too.
But words can't speak themselves,
They must be spoken,
And in court, the people that speak them, matter.
There is a Latin term for an argument made
Upon the man, rather than his words –
Ad hominem, the idea being
That such a form is fallacious,
That we should judge not the person
But the soundness of his reasonings.
In our daily lives, we do form opinions based on character,
And you might say we do worse.
We form opinions based on:
Facial expressions, tone of voice,
Gestures and so forth –
Even on a person's choice of clothes!
And why not – after all, the world's a slippery place?
We need every scrap
That might help us make sense.

But in a court of law
One would expect *Ad hominem*
Not to be allowed to rear its head.
And so from ancient Rome, comes Lustitia
Personified in blindfolded Lady Justice,
Holding a sword,
Weighing the evidence in her scales.
But we do look at the people in court.
We look at their expressions.
The defence lawyer is an older man
He is black and his delivery has gravity.
The lawyer for the prosecution
– a white man – appears considerably younger
Is earnest, if not inexperienced.
This is how it might appear.

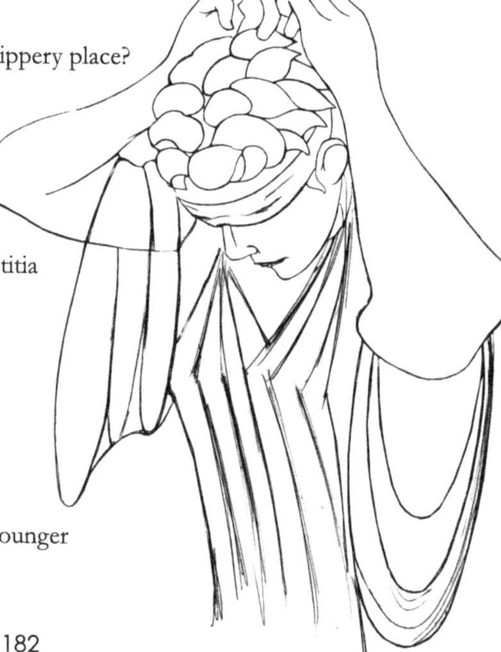

Then there is the Defendant…
It occurs to me that all the while the trial
Is in progress, one is disinclined
To turn and look at him in the dock.
Only when he took the stand did we
Listen to him and look at him.
Why is that?
Here, seeing people matters,
As it would anywhere.
We are even directed by the lawyers
To consider the way evidence is given.

Towards the end of Defence's,
Summing up, we are directed to look at the Defendant:
Making us absolutely aware that,
On the end of our decision – our verdict –
There will be a person – this person –
Who has been charged with a serious crime,
And that we have a responsibility,
To return the right verdict –
According to Defence,
One of 'Not guilty'.

So gradually is the jury coralled –
Hemmed in on all sides, as it were –
By evidence, by reasoned argument,
And by persuasion, until it is near to
Facing the final responsibility.

But the ultimate influence
Comes from the judge,
On the morning of the final day,
As he directs us by way of flow-chart logic alone.
According to this, much so-called evidence
Falls away. The story, such that it was in my mind,
Now becomes almost entirely irrelevant,
As the judge focuses our attentions
On the legal crux of the matter:
The identification beyond all reasonable doubt,
Of the Defendant at the scene of the crime
Or otherwise.
So then do we go away and deliberate...

During my time in court, more costs come to mind:
Of the gowns and wigs and court trappings;
Overheads of running such a building;
Training of legal minds;
Brain power expended on legal argument;
A jury's time away from its places of work;
To the employer of a juror in hours lost;
Of legal and penal systems to its taxpayers;
To convicted criminals and society
As they try to become rehabilitated.
Then there are the costs to the victims of crime,
And to their families,
Paid in lives wrecked, confidence lost, fear –
Incalculable costs.

Surely, crime benefits no-one.
If we have creativity on one hand,
Crime is its antithesis –
Destructive and of no use to society.
But I wonder what a place where
There was no crime would look like?
Would it be a place of perfect equipoise,
Peaceful, free of strivings,
Or would it be an anodyne one,
Of stagnation and carelessness?

We are ready.
We are called once more to court.
Spokesperson for the jury is asked
If the jury has reached a verdict.
He says that it has.
Is asked: 'On the charge of aggravated burglary,
How do you find the Defendant.'
He takes from his pocket
The piece of folded paper,
Where is written,
Our verdict
And reads it out.

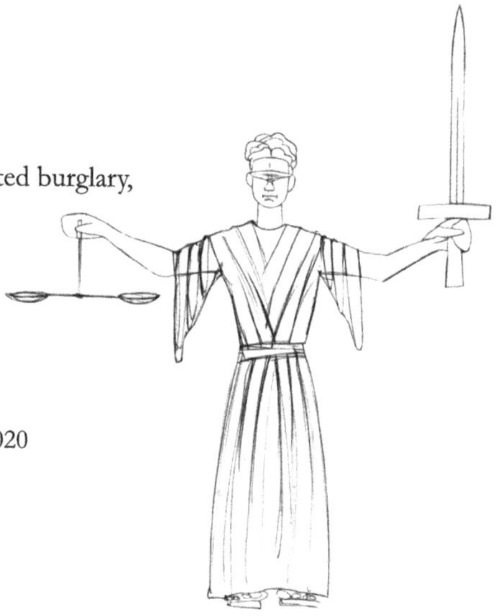

February 2020

Epilogue: The Secret River

The poem near the start of this book ('A River') became the inevitable provocation to go and take a look at the source of the Thames. So in late August 2019 (29th to be precise) that was what I did. After printing out a few screenshots from Google maps pinpointing the source – south of Cirencester on the East side of the A433 – and having noted there the establishment going by the name of 'The Thames Head Inn', I set off to drive the approx 200 miles from Cheshire, where I live. My sole aim was to take some photos – with the intention of using some to illustrate the poem. My camera battery was charged, spare at the ready, copy of the poem there to refer to if necessary, and blanket thrown in just case I needed to catch a few hours' sleep. (I planned to get there, do something of a recce, operate the camera, and drive back – the intention being to return perhaps twice more to the middle Thames to wrap it up.)

After a brief stop at the M5 Frankley Services to grab an M&S prawn sandwich (for me an extravagant but delicious purchase, greatly appreciated) and more importantly, buy an AA atlas of Britain, I arrived in the vicinity at around 3:15 afternoon. After already having been pushed along by a lorry making me go faster than I wanted to in order to get a good look at the sides of the road in the hope of spotting some likely lay-by or turning that would signal the start of my search, I decided to pull into the car park of 'The Thames Head Inn'. I consulted map and print outs but was none the wiser as to where I might park closer, other than seeing that there were some small white roads – lanes – that might take me somewhere near the source. (I didn't go into the pub because I didn't want to take what would, in my opinion, have been another backwards step of having to buy something – a drink which I didn't need – before making some progress in my aim i.e. at least one snap pertinent to the cause! If I wasn't a paying customer, I couldn't park. But I'd certainly come back later – as a reward, job done.)

But as good an ally as the car was in bringing me the 200 miles, it became a real impediment in the small-scale stuff now needed. First there was the ominous Dangerous Bridge whose tall but narrow arch is only wide enough to take one lane of traffic, so that oncoming cars must wait, and through which I passed only to find some safety highway maintenance vehicle (albeit with warning lights flashing) parked-up immediately on the other side – ironically itself creating a dangerous obstacle in an already dangerous place! And behind which I had to wait while the driver got in and then pulled away, only to creep forwards a few more metres before stopping again and waiting for me to overtake. I quite rightly hesitated, as to overtake would require me to drive into the path of any oncoming traffic on the approach to what was a totally blind summit. Was the man mad?! I gesticulated to him – 'how the hell was I supposed to get past?' (He could have given me a signal that all was clear but didn't seem to see the issue!) In the end I chanced it and got past. Probably – probably! – he knew it was clear, but didn't think fit to tell me. I don't know for sure.

Now I had vehicles behind me eager to make up for lost time, and so again was I pushed from pillar to post, not having time to look safely, so not properly, at the sides of the roads. I took a turning on my left as being about in the right place. Here I soon started to appreciate the Cotswold countryside: rolling fields – some grazing, some stubble – oaks and lovely little buildings of buttermilk-coloured stone. I took a little turning into a village with a quaint clock on the wall – 3:40. Pulled in there to see if there was someone I could ask the question: 'Do you know where I can find the source of the Thames?' but there were no humans in sight.

I turned round, went back to the road I'd come on and followed it further along as it twisted and turned, becoming more and more unlikely-looking. Coming upon a large grain store where there were tractors and lorries – some human activity – as well as space to turn round, I pulled in.

Two lads came over friendly enough. I told them what I was looking for and after a confab between themselves, they reckoned on some layby along the Tetbury-Kemble road as being what I was after, and gave me directions. I was in half a mind to ask if I could use their toilet to take a leak, but thought it a bit too cheeky – and so got in my car and drove off.

I'm never good with directions – unable to keep in my head more than about 3 or 4 'left then right's' as being the basic bits that have to be followed and perhaps a 'roundabout' and possibly a 'traffic lights' but usually dismissing as if not irrelevant but likely to interfere with essentials, all the helpful descriptions of significant landmarks that the directions-giver has kindly given.

Perhaps I should say at this stage that I don't have a smart phone or, perhaps more truthfully, don't use a smart phone in so much as I do own what I would call a 'mobile phone' that isn't very smart and that I rarely use (perhaps once a year) – a very deliberate choice so as not to (as I see it) be enslaved by a device that seems to control and zombify a large proportion of the world's population or, for that matter, feel I am the sap of huge multi-corporate advertising campaigns engineered to make us feel that if we don't have the latest gizmo, we are somehow weirdos. If I'm going to be a weirdo, then I'll do it on my own terms, thank you very much! That said, I appreciate that by making that choice, I make life difficult for myself, estranged as I am from the majority, as well as bereft of the excellent uses to which these devices can be put – such as telling the emergency services that one is lying injured up some Chilean mountain path, or using it extricate oneself from the Cotswolds. (To be honest, I can't really afford to run one.)

So then I'm following instructions as best I can and (I think) heading back in the direction of Cirencester but taking so long to reach the roundabout that I start wondering if I have misremembered the first instruction to 'turn right', and that I should have gone left. I'm just wondering whether I shouldn't go back to the point where I think I made the error and follow instructions in the opposite direction, when I see some speed restriction signs that I remember being mentioned; then comes the roundabout, where I follow the turning as instructed and realize I am back on the road with the Dangerous Bridge, but before the bridge there is the left turn that has been recommended and which I now take. 'Ah!' I think, feeling immediately better, 'So that was where I went wrong!' (Funny how the complexion on things changes when you feel you are once again in control.)

But by this stage I really do need a pee, and my head is sweating. Again I try to look for laybys, but again there are lots of cars behind, pushing me along dreadfully fast for such a small road. I pass some white wooden planks marking the start of Kemble village, and as I pass a couple of pull-ins if not laybys, wonder if it could be those?

But of course, there was no time to indicate to stop. Through Kemble am I legitimately (and even commendably) able to slow and look about for signs of a river, but can see none, then the speed limit changes as we're out the other side and I'm driving off faster, annoyed by the cars behind. 'Look!' I say, as my speedo climbs, 'I can go fast if I want, it's just that I'm looking for the source of the Thames you stupid morons!' Past an airfield, I pull into a little industrial estate, mop my forehead and clean my glasses. A friendly face bobs out from one of the units: "Can I help you?"

"Rather an odd question I know," say I (by way of an apologetic preface to one who clearly has more important things to do on a working Thursday afternoon than worrying about trivial tributaries) "but you don't happen to know where the source of Thames is, do you?"

"I'm sorry – you're asking the wrong person. I'm from Cheshire."

"Oh," I say, "I've just driven from there!"

"Whereabouts?"

"Er, Nantwich."

"Oh, I'm from Northwich."

"Oh, er, the Weaver's a bit easier to find that this," I joke.

The man recommends I ask at 'The Thames Head pub' – which it looks as if it is what I'll have to do!

Driving back along the Kemble road, I look across the fields to my left and see, running parallel for a little while, what looks as though it could be the course of some old stream – just a dry grassy depression in a meadow. A thought crosses my mind: I wonder if... But I expel it! I must take a leak!

Back through the Dangerous Bridge, and on to the carpark and bursting now, only one thing for it – I'll have to go in and buy a drink. There are few cars on the carpark. I wonder if the pub's open. There is a door at the side slightly open but I don't like to just walk in – might think I'm a sneak-thief, or something. There's another open door where I can hear someone washing plates and generally clattering about. But I can't see them. So I call: "Halloo there!" No reply. I call again: "Hallooo!" – no reply. After the fourth time of hallooing extremely and unnecessarily loudly (as it seems to me), out comes a woman, who apologises. (Though I get the distinct impression she might well have been listening for some time.) I ask if they are open. They are. So I wander into a nice pub. With over an hour gone and no closer to finding the source of the Thames, I order a coffee – something to wake me up and perhaps bring a bit of the alertness so far lacking – and while it is being made, go for a much-needed pee.

"I get asked that a lot!" says a young woman, my having asked the question of the day. "There's a track up the side of the bridge, I'll show you on the map." – which she does – a red line in felt tip pen, leading to a cross about a mile away. "Of course, it's dry at the moment. But it's fairly easy to find – well, no-one has ever come back and said they haven't!"

Hmm. I say that there's a first time for everything – pointing out that I am not very good at following directions. Armed with bag and camera but forgetting my hat, I set off.

It would be plain-sailing, but for a short stretch of tricky and dangerous road-walking to connect the pub with the start of the track – leading down to the Dangerous Bridge, in fact! So first I elect to cross and face the traffic. Snag is, cars coming under the bridge can't see me straight away, and are surprised when they do, and so I dart pretty well straight back, taking my chances with an occasional nervous glance over my shoulder to check for traffic behind. After a couple of scary moments as cars fly by hair-shavingly close to my shins, I make the start of the track. Phew! (What is it about people that when once they step inside their metal containers they become de-humanized killing machines?)

The first part runs alongside the railway – a rather shabby, cindery path with butterflies and lots of wild flowers and a scarpering rabbit or two – on until the point where the path crosses the main line that I take to run from Cirencester to Bath but am not at all sure about. Then on the other side, the landscape opens out across… not exactly a valley – though it does go down on my side – but no discernible topography that says: 'Hey, I'm a river valley!' There's a field of earth and a crop I can't identify – perhaps already harvested? – alongside which I pass and then another stile and a meadow with a few old oaks and ashes dotted about that is clearly grazed. Now which way? Trying to recollect the map on the wall, I remember the young woman's suggestion: 'You could take a picture of it.' (Assuming I had a smart phone, I guess – pretty useful things those darned smart phones!) I have a rough idea of where I should be headed – somewhere up ahead – but why can't I see the beginnings of a river coming back towards me – even a dry one? There's nothing here.

A little to the north is a stile coming in roughly from where the river ought to be running (I think), and a stocky post with a yellow top. I go and investigate. Various little oval labels screwed to the post tell me this is a part of the Wysis Way leading to Offa's Dyke, connecting with Thames Path. So now turning through 90 degrees and facing west, I head along what appears to be a hint of a track – perhaps made by cattle – but what ought, logically to my mind at least, to be a river – except that, if anything, it is raised slightly! In the distance I see some cattle on a hill with a curiously-profiled barn behind them. Then just to the right, in line with the route I am taking, I make out a small buff-coloured oblong that could possibly be a stone – possibly The Stone. I have already taken a few snaps but now the unashamed acquisitive image-grasping instinct that has accompanied the project so far, tells me I should start revving-up on what I came here to do and, every 20 metres or so, take a snap as I close in on what I am pretty sure is now the stone that marks the source of the River Thames.

There is a little round 'well' of oval stones that people have placed there and behind, the oblong slab of whatever it is – quartz perhaps? With its inscription, giving much the same impression as a new headstone in a graveyard. To the left is the signpost – again nicely crafted, that probably cost an arm and a leg – with various pointers, including one telling 'us' the Thames Barrier is 184 miles in 'that' direction. I take another snap in 'that' direction. The woman at the pub was right – it's dry enough. I have my doubts about this! There's no sign of a river or even a dry river bed – it's just a field. But it is August and I guess that in winter water does run here – somewhere. Then, to the right-hand side of the stone on its base, I notice (aha!) a damp patch. In the call of duty I go down on hands and knees and start ferreting about . Is it possible, I wonder?

Perhaps this spot really is the very source where a spring forces itself up from beneath – that patch the sign of its irrepressible urge to wet its surroundings, no matter how heavy the stone on top! (Go-on, my son!) This is what I think until I see a couple approaching, no doubt wondering what I'm doing grovelling on hands and knees – perhaps thinking it is the over-zealous attentions of a river-worshipper paying homage! We say hello and, partially to excuse my eccentric behaviour, I make known my theory concerning the damp patch, only to have it dashed when they tell me it rained hard overnight – and that it is probably a puddle that, being in the shadow of the rock has not entirely evaporated away. (The sun is now very strong and seeing the hat the man is wearing reminds me of my own deficit.) They tell me about a little bridge further up and the site of some Iron Age fort, and so we part ways as I trudge on a little further to investigate, ruminating as I go.

The stone has generated more questions than it has answered! Okay, so there's this: about a hundred-and-something miles down 'that way' is a great river thundering by the Houses of Parliament. Where the hell does it actually start? Because clearly, today at least, it doesn't start here! Or perhaps it's underneath – underground – but can a river run under a river bed? And anyway, there isn't even a bed to run under – it's just a bloody field! It feels almost as though it's some kind of elaborate tourist-trap hoax – except that I know it's not.

I make my way alongside what I take to be the site of the ancient fort, and peer over a little gate: deep wood, green-black, bird-song unidentifiable to my uneducated ears – a tangle of dark magic possibly, certainly mysterious and slightly foreboding.

I come to the bridge the couple have mentioned and look over – lots of fly-tipped black bin liners in the dappled shade. What sort of bastard does that? It looks a bit like the bed of a canal or a disused railway line. Except, as the sign says – this is the start of Offa's Dyke – although at this moment, with great gaps in my almost non-existent knowledge of history, that doesn't mean much.

I know what the function of a dyke is but I'm not sure whether there should or shouldn't be water involved somewhere in this one – no doubt a matter cleared up in seconds with a pesky smart phone! I sit for a moment by a sandy bank. Sans hat and drink, and with the sun beating down, I feel mentally disorientated and thirsty. I get up and make my way back to the stone.

Another couple (whom I'd put at about retirement age – whatever that means these days) have arrived and are pouring out each a glass from a small bottle of champagne – a celebration of some special occasion. I ask them, have they come far? 'From the Thames Barrier,' they say. Wow! I'm impressed. They've made the journey over the space of 16 days – a bit over 10 miles a day. They ask if I'd mind taking a snap of them together – I'd be glad to – but I do have some problem it seems, with the simple task of pressing 'the big white button' plum in the middle of the smart phone screen. In return I take the opportunity of trying to get an answer to the thing that is bugging me most: "I wonder: d'you happen to know where the point at which the river has some water in it, is?"

The man explains that it is on the other side of the road about two stiles across – he's made a note on his map: 'nearly dry'. But coming at this from different directions as we are, I am momentarily confused, and I say: "But is there some water there that you can actually see?" And he reiterates: "Yes – it's nearly dry." Ah, and then I realize: from their perspective it has been water all the way – they have been searching for the point at which the great river dries up. Momentarily, my aim slid by theirs. It's the water I need!

This is significant. It is nearly 5:30 PM GMT. Right now it is running through Greenwich, but not here. This stone really has nothing to do with the river – the river doesn't respect it. My head is burning from the sun. The cattle remain perched high on the mound and with the bullock on the summit standing stock still, the experience is like witnessing some kind of pastoral scene from an 18th Century English landscape painting, but with the added heat, it's shimmeringly surreal. There is work to be done! I thank the couple and walk on.

First I return to the pub to get my hat and have a well-iced lemonade. Then I must negotiate on foot not only the dangerous road again, but this time (if I don't want to walk back the way I've just come) actually pass under the Dangerous Bridge.

If you do come here, I advise you not to do what I just did – that bridge is deadly – there are chipped corners at the edges where vehicles have hit it and if you walk through you are in serious danger of being squished – stone dead!

Crossing a stile, I link with the Wysis Way on the Eastern side of the A433. Now there is – perhaps for the first time, a sense of purpose – a feeling of closing with something – not the source of the river, which is elusive and might be anywhere, but the start of the river.

But first I need something river-shaped, and here, as far as I can see, is just another meadow. Again, I apply a bit of logic: water flows down hill. If there is low-lying ground, that's where a river will be. Ah yes, but water is sneaky. I mean, you do get rivers up hills and mountains – flowing down them, sure – but up there in the first darned place! Water finds its own way, connecting one low bit to the next lower bit and so on. Anyway, any attempt to try to assess the topography of the ground by sight alone is likely to be unreliable. A good golfer might have the knack. But I don't play golf! But hey – the clue's in the name: 'Thames Path'. According to the post, that's what this will become. There is at least a path to follow. The path, of course, doesn't interest me – glad there's a way in so much as there's access – but it's the physical sign of the presence of a river, I need.

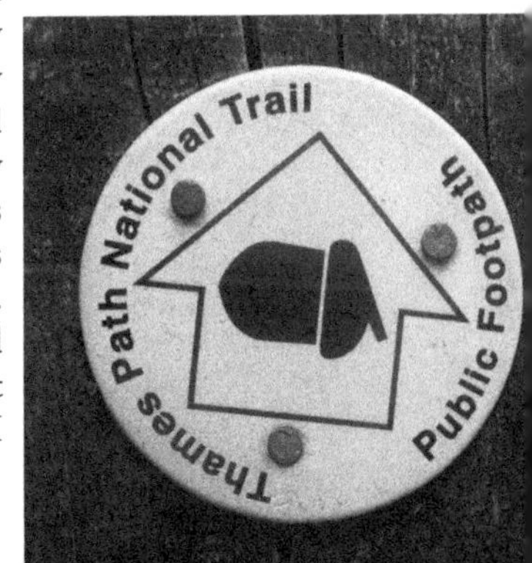

Perhaps a third of the way through the first field, I come upon a wavy edge to the grass – as though the path side might at some point have been mown to make it wavy. But I know it is not mowing that has caused the change. Something there makes it grow differently – a band of slightly longer grass with a sinuous shadow running through – a 'snake' in the grass! Hmm, okay, but it's still just grass, and bone dry – rivers aren't made of grass! Anyway, then it disappears and we're back to just field. About 30m ahead I can see something happening again – a band of longer, slightly drier grass with the occasional brown dried up dock leaf(?) at the side. When I reach the spot where this starts there are several largish stones, half as big as a football in there – like ones you might get somewhere along a river bed.

Further on comes a different grass, broader-leaved more like a reed but not a reed – sedge, perhaps? – and in there many little round pink flowers – mallows? Again, I walk across and back, and again, though the ground goes down a few inches and back up, it is firm all the way. The nature of this band made up of a variety of wild plants is the only thing that enables me to differentiate between the rest of the meadow and what might be the whisper of a river. It is as though there is some shallow watercourse here whose element has been converted temporarily from mineral to vegetable. Three hours since my arrival and still nothing conclusive! But I know what evidence I need or, at least, I think I do.

Towards the end of the first meadow comes an abrupt change where (let's say) sedge gives way almost entirely to reeds and then a depression covered in a net of convolvulus becomes a little deeper towards the mouth of a culvert going under a concrete track. Now at this point, although still dry, it is like: 'You just stop me trying to be a river!' But over the track, just beyond is a little thicket of trees, across which there appears to run a low dry-stone wall – a curious and for the moment, unsettling thing, because if what I have so far been following is the beginning of an as yet waterless watercourse, then here would appear to be an obstacle across its path! Whoever heard of a river flowing through a wall? I push on to investigate. What I find delights me…

A wall it is yes, of sorts, but with holes through, and on the other side do I see what is unmistakably the dried-up pool of a small river. I walk on to a bed of flat stones and turn to face 'upstream' and the wall – in fact, what must be, when the river flows here, a low weir, and a rather lovely thing.

Growing all along its base and hanging from each of the apertures like beards is desiccated, dark green waterweed. It is as though the weed is the water petrified – again in vegetable form! I thought the evidence I needed was presence of water. But I was wrong. This is almost as good. I can see the nooks and crannies in the stones under the weed where, when the pool is full, perch and eels and trout might hide. Heartened by this discovery, I start to walk along the river bed. Somewhere there will be water.

But this river is full of surprises! Now come patches of fine gravel – white granules chalky in appearance, almost like particles of hard cement and bone dry. Here the riverbed has all the appearance of a disused railway track! Clearly, under the gravel is moisture for there are numerous plants. Again I wonder: is it possible for a river to flow under its own bed – as a kind of river upside down? But the idea is absurd!

I push on and then under some willows, the ground feels softer. I push hard against it, feeling my foot sinking in, slightly. Here are many plants and then just up ahead glistening between the weeds comes the first unmistakable glimpse of the essential element – water lying just a few millimetres deep! Then it's gone. I push on, and emerge from under the willows to the barking of dogs – a couple of excitable boxers romp into view. Here is a track leading off from our field, dipping first into the river's course and away into the next field. The dip is a ford – a gravel depression. In it lies a decent small pool of clear water through which the dogs run – splashing and drinking appreciatively, as they go. I ask the owner has he seen the river when it flows? He says he's only just moved here and not yet seen it in other seasons. He says that the water in the pool has only just come. I walk on. Another thought comes: perhaps this is just the residue after last night's downpour – not true river water at all! Boy, does this river give up its secrets slowly!

Then a road comes in from the left and starts to run parallel. In the distance I see the white wooden planks that mark the entrance to Kemble village. I realize, that what I'd first seen getting on for 4 hours ago from the car window, as I drove about frantically and disorientated, was indeed the Thames riverbed. I just needed to introduce myself to it at closer quarters and on foot to realize it. Here is where the river passes under the road by way of the first substantial bridge – one of small gloomy double arches. No doubt, this is where the lads were trying to direct me. All is bone dry.

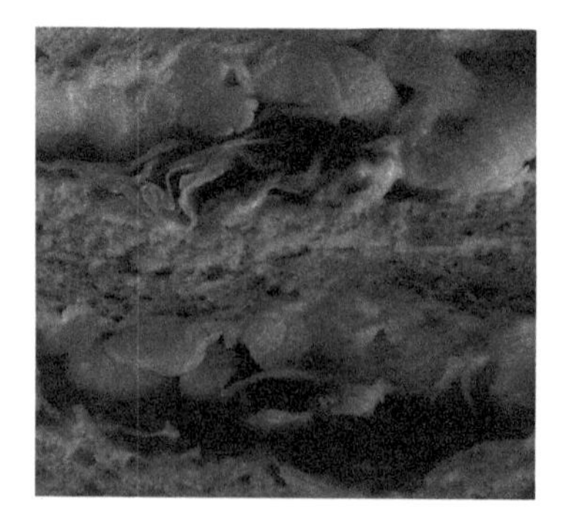

But now already the light is beginning to go a little and I have yet to walk back and, if I'm to avoid sleeping in the car, drive back to Cheshire. If truth be known, I don't do much walking (far too little to be healthy, even) and though I've walked only a few miles, my legs are feeling it. Though I've only scratched the surface of what I'd set out to do picture-wise, in some ways I've achieved far more – I'm glad the river is playing so hard to get! 'Where does it start flowing?' I wonder – can I reach it before I have to turn back? I cross over the road, deciding to explore a little further.

To the eastern side the watercourse starts to look more like the bed of a small river. In some places are there discernible, gently-sloping banks and pebble-bottomed pools where the roots of trees would drink – but all as yet waterless and with no sign of it appearing any time soon. Still the thought of the great river flowing now through London comes to me. I wonder: what if there is some tributary stream that meets hereabouts causing the flow to suddenly start? Why then it would be named 'Thames' kind of by deed poll only! If that was the case, then over the seasons and the years, more rightly ought not a river's name to change according to its true source? How confusing would that be? But perhaps the river is named not at its birth but where it enters the sea, as a body with a clear identity – at its end. Traced upstream, clearly it will be the same river, and only eventually will there be some point where its identity becomes uncertain? Perhaps, this river will start to flow entirely of its own volition – I do hope so – but can't imagine how the water will appear. Vowing to come back and take up the search again as soon as I can, I turn about and begin the walk (if a little stiffly) back to the remaining half a prawn sandwich, no doubt itself tested stiffly by the sun.

I'd like to say that when I returned again (4 days later) I took up the path where I left off, except this would not be true. I wanted to take a few snaps to fill in with what has already gone so far – and did, and you'll have seen them with the text. But then I might have just driven to Kemble and taken again the path downstream from the bridge there.

My mistake was in trying to second guess the river by anticipating that it would not run until Ewen – a small village, perhaps a couple of miles from Kemble. And so I decided to start there. My decision to do so was no doubt influenced by the 4-day hiatus, so that my original mind-set – a slightly obsessive one – had gone – the 'spell' broken.

Of course I needn't have told you any of this, connecting what comes (er...) seamlessly with the earlier narrative! But to me this has been about truth and veracity – the experience of seeing the little beginning of a great river 'sent off' properly! Whether it has to do with an ever-shifting background of uncertainty – politics in turmoil, democratic constitution in crisis, looming prorogation – I don't know. Perhaps! Maybe it's like wanting to find at least one thing one can be sure of. Whatever the motivation, I drove to Ewen and then, with that same fumbling ineptitude common to part one, set off uncertainly down a lane to arrive 5 minutes later at a little bridge, signposted for 'Thames Path'.

Here was shallow water running at the backs of houses – perhaps an inch deep but which I could see from its riffling surface, was running! Yes, in one way it was exciting – it had started, it was on its way (and it had pulled a fast one)! But in another, it was disappointing – I might as well have impulsively jumped in the car and driven to (say) Oxford, and seen it running there, for all the good it had done. No, I was getting ahead of myself. I decided to make amends by following it back where I had been 4 days earlier and find that point where it started to flow. For all I knew, it might still be by way of some spring-fed tributary usurper! I owed it to what had gone so far, to find out...

Upstream of this bridge there is a portion of land where the path cannot follow, the river passing around a field of bullocks and then private housing and mill, so that the path joins the river again alongside School Road perhaps half a mile on. Here I follow it beneath the trees, seeing it all the while shallow and slow but (fortunately) still flowing. At the other end was another bridge.

Looking over the parapet and upstream is like looking on water flowing in a bed of cress – wet enough! I stop briefly to speak to a man walking his spaniel – a water-loving breed whose interests will no doubt keep its owner closely connected with the riverbanks as his dog rushes in and out. He tells me of a spot where the water comes and goes 'just the watertable,' he says. (Sounds promising!)

So now I follow through a special meadow, kept this way, I guess, for bees and honey-making, for here are tall clover and little pockets of wild flowers – daisies, cornflower and yellow trefoil(?) overall with the slightly dark and 'understated' beauty that somehow reminds me of a mediaeval tapestry. To the left is the river beneath an impenetrable canopy of high-key (almost acid) green – with a net of convolvulus right over the top for good measure. The canopy (I guess) is a clue to the presence of water – bringer of life. Gradually as I reach the end of this field, the canopy thins. There are still trees, but now gaps appear. And it is through one of these that I pass and drop down on to the river bed. Here are pebbles and flat stones, roots, and just here and there wet patches – barely pools, really. I walk upstream, checking each one as I go.

Now one has to scrutinize the water for movement. It might move for several reasons: because a draught of air brushes its surface, because insects skip and skim upon it. Perhaps the biggest distraction is the reflections of wind-blown willow leaves waving in the canopy overhead, that make the water itself appear to flicker animatedly. All of these have to be separated out and set aside until there is left only one which, when it is perceived, is unmistakable – the creeping motion of a living river. I take this one patch to be the last, but only when I have walked further upstream to make absolutely sure, do I return with certainty to photograph it, so you can see it here – the start of the River Thames, on this day, at least! I know now that the water I had seen on my first visit was indeed rainwater.

Still pushing on further upstream I meet a few more pools – and a surprisingly deep one that has almost the look of a blue-green pool of a jungle rainforest, a place where local swimmers might go at another part of the year – if they could brave the cold? But all of these are lifeless and still, if not stagnant. Walking on with the cornfield to my right, I come eventually upon the part I had walked a few evenings ago, my search at an end.

I realize now the mystery had been solved when I found the little waterless weir. And sure enough I realize (from the point of view of one with no knowledge of physical geography) that a river does in some sense flow beneath the bed, seeping there and connecting those places where, just occasionally, the bed is low enough for it to emerge. So the river's way is made of earth – the way the land lies. The elemental water, much deeper, beholden to nothing and coming from beyond the river's banks, makes of the earth its own way through the land. It's us that calls it 'river'. In truth the water respects no boundaries, as when it bursts its banks and floods.

Perhaps that wrong way of thinking about it has to do with our for so long shaping waterways by engineering – building embankments in towns and cities, dredging, cutting, clearing, installing pumps and sluices – so we begin to feel that we, rather than nature is in control and, dare I say, because of that, lacking humility. Well, the floods of recent years are overwhelmingly humbling enough to change our minds on that one...!

Just before returning home, I walked downstream from Ewen to a little weir over which, even in high summer, the river poured with great promise. I wondered how long it would take the water flowing there to reach the Houses of Parliament and when it did, whether some decision would have been made on the future of this land. Silly me! September 2019

Dedication: to everyone outside of the golden cage (excluding me but with whom I stand) and to anyone inside trying to escape. ('Psst! – the door ain't locked – come and join us.')

Credits: all text and images are by the author unless otherwise stated. Some lines in 'Mac is Back' taken from Bertolt Brecht's lyrics from 'Mack the Knife', 'The Threepenny Opera'. Credit and thanks must go to writer and poet, Penny Kimber, who not only kindly helped to proof read text but suggested many changes that have improved sense and readability.